ENGLISH MEN OF LETTERS

EDITED BY JOHN MORLEY

WILLIAM HAZLITT

ENGLISH MEN OF LETTERS

WILLIAM HAZLITT

BY

AUGUSTINE BIRRELL

*" A man's life is his whole life, not the
last glimmering snuff of the candle"*

GREENWOOD PRESS, PUBLISHERS
WESTPORT, CONNECTICUT

Originally published in 1902
by The Macmillan Company

First Greenwood Reprinting 1970

SBN 8371-2848-X

PREFACE

THE chief authorities for this *Life of Hazlitt* are the following: —

(1) Hazlitt's own books.

(2) *Literary Remains of the late William Hazlitt: With a Notice of his Life by his Son, and Thoughts on his Genius and Writings*, by E. L. Bulwer, Esq., M.P., and Mr. Serjeant Talfourd. In two volumes, Saunders and Ottley, 1836.

(3) *Memoirs of William Hazlitt*, by W. Carew Hazlitt (grandson). Two volumes, Richard Bentley, 1867. This book is cited as *Life*.

(4) *Four Generations of a Literary Family*, by W. Carew Hazlitt. Two volumes. George Redway, 1897. This book is cited as *Hazlitt Memoirs*.

(5) *Lamb and Hazlitt*. Edited by W. Carew Hazlitt. Elkin Matthews, 1900.

(6) List of the Writings of William Hazlitt and Leigh Hunt, chronologically arranged and with notes, by Alexander Ireland. John Russell Smith, 1868.

(7) *William Hazlitt, Essayist and Critic.* With Memoir by Alexander Ireland. Frederick Warne and Co., 1889.

(8) A privately printed edition of the *Liber Amoris*, containing Mrs. Hazlitt's *Journal of my Trip to Scotland.* 1894.

With regard to (3), (4), and (5), I have to thank Hazlitt's grandson, Mr. W. Carew Hazlitt, for his permission, most cordially extended to me, to make such use as I have done of these authorities. Without that permission I should not have felt at ease in handling the valuable materials they contain.

A. B.

3 New Square, Lincoln's Inn,
     November 23, 1901.

CONTENTS

CHAPTER I

PAGE

PARENTAGE — BIRTH — AND THE UNITED STATES OF
AMERICA 1

CHAPTER II

WEM 17

CHAPTER III

COLERIDGE 38

CHAPTER IV

THE LOUVRE 56

CHAPTER V

FIRST BOOKS, MARRIAGE, AND LONDON 73

CHAPTER VI

THE BEGINNING OF STRIFE 95

CHAPTER VII

LIFE AND LECTURES 115

CHAPTER VIII

PAGE

QUARRELS, ESSAYS, DELUSIONS, AND PICTURE GALLERIES 143

CHAPTER IX

MAXIMS, TRAVELS, AND *THE SPIRIT OF THE AGE* . . 181

CHAPTER X

THE END OF STRIFE 206

CHAPTER XI

CHARACTER AND GENIUS 226

WILLIAM HAZLITT

WILLIAM HAZLITT

CHAPTER I

It was the belief of Hazlitt's son, an amiable and accomplished Registrar of the old Court of Bankruptcy, that the name his father made illustrious was of Dutch origin, and originally spelt Haesluyt. The diligent researches of the grandson, Mr. W. Carew Hazlitt, would not, however, justify the most conscientious of biographers in crossing a stormy sea to explore the ancient burying places of Haarlem and Leyden in search of the progenitors of the writer and critic whose passage through life has here to be shortly recorded.

Cross the sea, however, that biographer must, but with his face turned to the west; for it is in a lone churchyard in the county of Tipperary that the bones lie of John Hazlitt and Margaret his wife, the grandparents of the famous writer, and farther back one cannot safely go.

Tradition tells us of Hazlitts, or Hasletts, or even it may be of Haesluyts, who shortly after the days of Dutch William were to be found in Antrim and Coleraine and other northern parts of Ireland, pursuing various vocations, and adhering to the dominant Protestant religion, though affecting the Presbyterian colour. Whether these possible ancestors were " the noble, silent men" about whom Carlyle, that prince of biographers, loved to discourse in his early chapters, "scattered here and there, each in his department silently thinking, silently working," or the most arrant chatterboxes in all Ireland, nobody now knows. For us, at all events, they are as silent as even Carlyle could wish.

Some time, however, and 1735 is a likely date, John Hazlitt, a flax factor, left Antrim; and in the company of one John Damer, who grew rich, and upon whose fortune a nephew maintained an earldom, came south and established himself in business at Shronell, or Shrone-hill, in county Tipperary, near the town of the same name. John Hazlitt probably brought his wife Margaret with him; and on the 18th of April 1737 his eldest son was born at Shronell and baptized, according to the Presbyterian ritual, William. This William Hazlitt it was who in due time became the father of another William Hazlitt who has made the name familiar to our ears.

There were two other sons born to John and Margaret of Shronell — James and John. John emigrated to America in colonial days, but became on the first opportunity a rebel; and, distinguishing himself as a soldier, died a colonel and a citizen of the United States. This Colonel John Hazlitt must not be confused with another warrior of the same name and rank, who also took arms against King George, and died at the head of his regiment on the field of Preston, 1777. This second Colonel John

Hazlitt belonged to the Coleraine branch, and was accounted a cousin.

William Hazlitt the Elder, as I will usually call him by way of identification, remained in Ireland till his nineteenth year, when he went to the University of Glasgow, where, says his great-grandson, he had the good fortune to be contemporary with Adam Smith. Nothing is known now of William's university career except that he attended Professor Clow's Logic Class, and gave great satisfaction to Dr. Moor, the then Professor of Greek. He proceeded *Artium Magister* in due course. His younger brother James followed him to Glasgow, where he also graduated. The descendants of James are still living in Tipperary.

William the Elder's university education being completed in or about 1761, it became necessary for him to choose a vocation in life. This choice presented no difficulty. He belonged by the grace of God to the great and happy race of Parson Adams, whom he much resembled save in the accident of orthodoxy. When and how the elder Hazlitt became a Unitarian I have not learned. It may be that his mother, a thoughtful woman, who rejoiced that her firstborn should be a divine, had imbibed the subtle Arian heresy and transmitted it in a fiercer form to Professor Clow's pupil. A Unitarian, however, the elder Hazlitt became, being examined before he entered the ministry, and certified sound, by three eminent doctors of that faith — Dr. Price, Dr. Chandler, and Dr. Prior — all of whom he excelled in primitive fervour, republican zeal, and Hebraistical piety.

If ever a man scorned this world and the things belonging to it, William Hazlitt the Elder was that man; for in the pure white flame of his enthusiasm every shabby ambition, every mean and paltry aim, were shrivelled up before they had time to flutter. The impression he left upon his son, a born Epicurean in temperament, though not in philosophy, was tremendous, and is happily recorded in more than one passage of resounding vocables and true inspiration. I must but lightly pass over the adventures and characteristics of this fine old Nonconformist, but to ignore them altogether would be wrong; for they had a great share in making the Hazlitt I am most concerned with what he was as a writer, if not what he was as a man.

The history of the English Presbyterians during the eighteenth century and their lapse into Arianism and Unitarianism is well known. It has been elucidated in the Court of Chancery, and expounded by Macaulay in the House of Commons. Small endowments kept tiny congregations together despite the unpopularity of their tenets; their country ministers were frequently men of piety and learning, and usually imbued with a love of individual freedom and independent thought. They were almost always apostolically poor. During the bad times, when the eighteenth century came to an end, and the last century so heavily drew its early breath, the Unitarians were wholly an influence for good.

The elder Hazlitt's first congregation was at Wisbeach, in the Isle of Ely, where he went in 1764, and remained two years. Wisbeach was, and indeed is, a great place for Dissent. You may read of it in De Foe, the first political Dissenter. The Godwins, though originally from Yorkshire, were long settled in

Wisbeach, and the father of that grimy Gamaliel, the author of the *Political Justice*, was a predecessor of Hazlitt's at the Meeting House. The old Dissenting families of the neighbourhood cherished many stirring memories of persecution, toleration, and reaction; but of their own bigotry, when predominant, not a tradition was to be found, so much easier is it to remember your heroism under misfortune than your pride in place.

Out of one of these families the elder Hazlitt took a wife — Grace Loftus, whose father was an ironmonger in the market-place. The ironmonger had married an Oxfordshire lady, Grace Pentlow, who, though she was eleven years old when Queen Anne died, and remembered the news coming on a Sunday morning, and how greatly the Dissenters rejoiced as they repaired to the conventicles that had been threatened with compulsory closing, yet lived to the year 1801.

William Hazlitt and Grace Loftus were married on the 19th of January 1766 at Peterborough, in a parish church, which, unlike the Quakers, they were content to enter in order to preserve their children from the taint of bastardy. Grace Hazlitt, who, like her mother, lived to a great age, had many charms, and was reckoned very good-looking, though her marked resemblance in nose and lip to the younger Pitt is not by itself recommendatory of her person, and must have been a great trial to her son.

After his marriage, the elder Hazlitt and his young wife — she was twenty-two — moved to Marshfield, in Gloucestershire, where he ministered to the needs of a small number of heretical maltsters, and here his eldest son John (the painter) was born, as also was a boy Loftus, who died in early days.

In 1770 Hazlitt the Elder came to Maidstone, where he was minister of the Earle Street Meeting House, a somewhat important place in the small community to which he was proud to belong. Here he made friends, some of celebrity, such as Dr. Priestley, Dr. Kippis, and even Benjamin Franklin; but the elder Hazlitt, like his son, had no gifts for the great, and chose his companions for no better reason than because he enjoyed their society. His great cronies at Maidstone were Mr. Wiche, the Baptist minister, and Mr. Viny of Tenterden, at whose house it was he used to meet Franklin. Viny was Pro-English, and Hazlitt Pro-American, so there was no lack of conversation, which cannot have failed to be animated.

At Maidstone, on the 10th of April 1778, in a house no longer recognisable, in a lane once called Mitre, and now Bullock, William Hazlitt was born. On the 21st of June he was baptized by his father in the Meeting House; but, as he once said in words, the deep significance of which penetrate to the very core of his being, "I started in life with the French Revolution," and certainly there were always more traces of the Revolution about Hazlitt than of the rite of Christian Baptism.

Seven years earlier, but also at Maidstone, another child had been born, and a very useful member of the family she proved to be — Margaret, commonly called Peggy, whose family diary, copious extracts from which were published for the first time in the *Hazlitt Memoirs* (1897), is full of interest.

The travels and adventures of William Hazlitt the

Younger began early; for in 1780 his father, in consequence of one of those congregational quarrels which
are the weakness of Independency, had to leave Maidstone. He returned to Ireland, taking his family with
him, and for three years abode at Bandon, near Cork,
where, ever active in the cause of Humanity, and
never averse to being in a hopeless minority, he
pleaded with courage and success the cause of a number of American rebels who were exposed to great
hardships, and even wanton cruelty, at Kinsale
Prison.

These courageous and disinterested efforts made
Bandon an uncomfortable place for a man with a
young family; and the elder Hazlitt in 1783, and in
the face of strong advice to the contrary, given him
by Dr. Price, who had, at Hazlitt's instigation, sought
Lord Shelburne's assistance in the case of the Kinsale
prisoners, made up his mind to emigrate to America,
with whom a treaty of peace was about to be concluded. Accordingly, on the 3rd of April 1783, the
elder Hazlitt; his wife Grace Hazlitt; his son John,
then fifteen; his daughter Margaret, aged twelve;
William, just entering upon his sixth year; and a
little Harriet, born in Bandon, all sailed from Cork,
on board the *Henry* bound for New York, hoping to
find in the new Republic about to rise, as Peggy the
diarist expresses it, "a perfect land where no tyrants
were to rule, no bigots to hate and persecute their
brethren, no intrigues to feed the flame of discord and
fill the land with woe."

Paradise was farther off in those days than it is
now, for it was not until May the 12th, seven good
weeks, that the *Henry* sighted Long Island.

Hazlitt was thus destined to see New York before ever he set eyes on London. He is so essentially a child of the old world — of old plays, old books, old pictures, and old prejudices — that it is hard to think of him as living in a brand-new Republic across the Atlantic, as yet unenriched with any of the spoils of time.

The United States were not, however, to be more than an episode in the lives of the Hazlitts; and within little more than four years all of them, save little Harriet, who did not bear transplanting, and an Esther born in the States, who did not live to come home, were back again in benighted old England.

The scenery of the States did not make the impression one would expect upon the young William. From five to nine are usually impressionable years; and Hazlitt, above most men, made good play with all his impressions on paper. The diary of his sister is full of the trees and birds and landscape; but in Hazlitt's writings nothing of America remains but, little epicure that he was, the taste of barberries — *that* taste, he wrote, "I have in my mouth still after an interval of more than thirty years, for I have met no other taste in all that time at all like it." Perhaps Hazlitt's enthusiasms required the stimulus of a book in his hand or a picture on the wall. However this may be, these enthusiasms were kept virginal for the old world, for Rousseau, for Titian, for Mrs. Siddons, and for the range of lofty hills seen from Wem in pleasant Salop.

The adventures of a wandering Parson Adams of the Unitarian persuasion and his family in those new States, whither the very ship that brought them also

brought the first news of the peace with the old and
defeated country, as narrated in the diary of the eldest
daughter, are full of movement and almost romantic
interest; but they are not sufficiently relevant to the
main issue of this little book to justify more than a
reference. The diary might advantageously be edited
and published as a whole.

The arrival of the Hazlitts in New York created
great excitement, for the reason already given. " As
soon as we cast anchor," records the diarist, " we
were visited by some of the British officers, who came
on board eager to hear the news. Ours was the first
ship that brought an account of the treaty of peace.
And then how they raved and swore, cursing both the
Congress and those at home who had thus put a stop
to their ravaging with fire and sword their brothers'
land; and in this our most valiant captain most
piously joined, so much were their American brethren
transformed in their eyes (by that little, magical
word rebel) into bands of lawless banditti whom it
would be meritorious to destroy."

The family remained in New York but two days,
and then started for Philadelphia, resting by the way
at Burlington, where on Sunday Mr. Hazlitt, " by
special request," preached before the New Jersey
Assembly then in sitting, his first sermon on American
soil. It sounds very grand, but the service was con-
ducted in a small room with only benches to sit upon.
Mrs. Hazlitt would have liked to have remained at
Burlington, and to have opened a school there, a likely
project which might have made an American of
William Hazlitt, but the Divine had other aims than
school-mastering, and insisted upon pushing on to Phil-

adelphia. To this fair city, excellently well described
in Peggy's diary, the family journeyed in a stage-
waggon, driving for two days through the New Jersey
woods, "full of majestic trees mingled with the blossoms of the wild peach and apricot, and the sweet-
scented yellow flowers of the locust-trees perfuming
the air."

In Philadelphia the Hazlitts remained fifteen
months, having hired a house in Union Street, for
which they paid £30 a year in English money. Immediately on arrival the elder Hazlitt and his son
John hurried off to St. Peter's Church, not to return
thanks for their safe arrival in the Land of Freedom,
but to catch a glimpse of Freedom's hero, General
Washington, who was attending church on some public
occasion.

They met in the neighbourhood other Hazlitts from
Coleraine, and heard about the Colonel John, of whom
mention has already been made.

The elder Hazlitt during his stay in Philadelphia
preached assiduously in such pulpits as were open to
him, but in the matter of Unitarianism the States
were not yet the Land of Freedom. Calvinistic orthodoxy was still installed in Church and College; and
Subscription, the bondage of the spirit, was as much
the fashion as in the old country. The presidency of
a college at Carlisle, with a stipend of £300 a year,
was offered Hazlitt, but on those terms of slavery.
His reply was that he would sooner die in a ditch
than submit to human authority in matters of faith.
The language is familiar, but Hazlitt meant what he
said. He had therefore to be content with the life of
a wandering preacher and lecturer on the Evidences

of Christianity, going wherever he was invited. On some of these occasions his little son William accompanied him even into the pulpit itself, where he would sit on a cushion at his father's feet, hid from sight, pursuing his own wandering thoughts, whilst far above his head he heard the familiar and beloved paternal voice unfolding and recounting his "dream of infinity and eternity, of death, the resurrection, and judgment to come."

To Boston indeed the elder Hazlitt almost received "a call." It seemed a settled thing, but it was not to be. "The persecuting zeal of the orthodox sent one of their chosen brethren after him, and thus put a stop to his settling there." The fact is, Hazlitt was a pioneer. He was perhaps the first professed Unitarian in the States which had not yet been visited and organised by Priestley. Unitarianism was to have its day in Boston, and to rule supreme at Harvard; but its day had not then arrived, and is now over, for I am given to understand that "a mild Episcopalianism" is the mode of religion found easiest of assimilation by the present inhabitants of Boston.

In August 1774 the Hazlitts left Philadelphia for a beautiful home in Weymouth, some fifteen miles from Boston.

"The house," so the diarist tells us, "stood in a most romantic spot, surrounded on three sides by very steep hills that sloped down just in sight of the windows, and were covered with locust-trees.

"These trees grow to a great height, and their yellow blossoms, somewhat like the laburnum, perfumed the air in spring. On the green before the door stood a solitary pear-tree, beyond the shade of which in the

hot days William was not allowed to go until four
o'clock, when the sun was in some sort shaded by the
neighbouring hills. On the pales that enclosed this
sloping green the woodpeckers were wont to sit, and
make a noise with their bills like a saw. Beyond the
garden and lane was a large meadow, which in the
summer evenings, with its myriads of fire-flies, made
a brilliant appearance.

"On a little low hill to the eastward stood the house
of prayer, and below it Dr. Tuft's, the road to Boston
passing close by them; to the north King-Oak Hill,
which in the winter, when covered with snow, reflected
the golden and purple tints of the setting sun. Over
this hill the road leading to Hingham was seen. . . .
The hills behind the house are very steep, and it was
one of our childish exploits, when they were covered
with ice, to climb up and write our names on the
frozen snow.

"From the top of these hills we had a distant view
of the Bay of Boston, and many of its islands and
hills beyond it, with Dorchester heights, famous for
the Battle of Kegs; Bunker's Hill, where so many
British officers fell in the space of five minutes, singled
out by the sharpshooters of the Yankees; to the south,
dark and frowning woods, and nearer to us the river,
with a mill and two houses on its banks, and a variety
of meadows, fields, and trees below. Here also was
seen the house of Captain Whitman, a good friend of
ours. He was so fond of William that the boy spent
half his time in going with him to the woods, or to the
fields to see them plough, or attending the milking of
the cows, where I, too, was often present. . . ."

A pleasant exterior, surely enough. Inside the

house "was a very large picture in oil of the meeting of Esau and Jacob. The embracing of the two brothers, the meeting of their followers on either side, with the groups of camels and other cattle, and the background wending up between the hills and seeming to vanish in the air completed the enchantment. On this picture I used to gaze with delight." So writes Peggy.

The picture was one of the early works of Copley, and though John Hazlitt, a bit of a painter himself by this time, affected to think little of it, one cannot doubt that the young William shared his sister's rapture, for "The Meeting of Esau and Jacob" must have been the first real canvas on which rested his devouring eye. It is strange he should never have mentioned it. In Peggy's account it is pleasant to recognise the family gusto, for she describes her one dull Copley with something of the same feeling that her little brother was in days to come to write of "that cold convent spire rising in the distance, amidst the blue sapphire mountains and the golden sky" of Titian's St. Peter Martyr, now, alas! no longer to be seen, and of many another famous picture in London, Paris, Florence, and Rome.

Long walks were things of necessity at Weymouth. Hingham, where the elder Hazlitt often preached, was five miles off. "How often," says the diarist, "have we stood at the window looking at my father as he went up the Hingham road with William in his nankeen dress marching by his side like one that could never be tired." Thus early was the boy initiated into the charm of the road! A great pedestrian he remained all his life. He envied no man his travelling-chariot. "Give me the clear blue sky over my head, and the green turf beneath my feet, a winding road before me and a three hours' march to dinner, and then to thinking. It is hard if I cannot start some game on these lone heaths. I laugh, I run, I leap, I sing for joy."

A man's life is his whole life, and it was memories like these of joyful, exultant existence that must have prompted the last words Hazlitt ever uttered after living the life I have to record, "Well — I have had a happy life."

Boston was beyond the six-year-old legs of William, but the elder Hazlitt and John thought nothing of a walk there and back, to preach or lecture, or see a Unitarian tract through the press. At Hingham, old Mr. Ebenezer Gay was minister, and there were those of his congregation who thought he might at ninety years of age retire, and make way for Mr. Hazlitt; but Mr. Gay, who was "a very pleasant old man," and "fond of a good story," did not share this view, though always glad to let his young brother preach for him whenever so minded. No settlement could be found. In the summer of 1785 Hazlitt tried Cape Cod, "a neat little town, established chiefly by fishermen, and nothing to be seen but rucks and sands and the boundless ocean." William was taken to Cape Cod, and on arriving he inquired whether any robins or Bob Lincolns came there, and on being told No, replied, "I suppose they do not like so ugly a place," which was a little hard on Cape Cod.

Romantic Weymouth was given up after a year and eight months, when the family found it convenient to live nearer to Boston. Upper Dorchester was their

new home, five miles from Boston — in a small house
on the high road. Hazlitt continued to preach as
before in Boston, Salem, Hingham, and other places,
but at last in despair he determined to go back home,
which he did by himself, sailing from Boston in
October 1786. He had not long been gone when old
Mr. Gay died, and the Meeting House at Hingham
might have been his. The diarist mourns over the
mischance, and whatever might have been her brothers'
lot, there can, I think, be little doubt that her life
would have been a happier one had she remained in
New England.

After the elder Hazlitt's departure, his family remained at Dorchester for eight months, John studying
painting as best he could, and teaching William, who
worked like a fury, his Latin Grammar. Mrs. Hazlitt,
wherever she went, was a great favourite, and they
had many friends in Boston and its neighbourhood.
On July 4, 1787, "the grand anniversary of American
Independence," this small family of baffled Radicals
sailed home, disembarking at Portsmouth on the 12th
of August. The stage-coach took them to London,
where they were joyfully received. After this fashion
did William Hazlitt reach London.

The earliest composition of Hazlitt's that has sur-
vived is a letter to his father in London, evidently
written from Dorchester. Letters of Hazlitt's are
great rarities, and his first must be given at length.
His many friends in America will find it easy to forgive.

"12th of Nov.

"My dear Papa, — I shall never forget that we came to
america. If we had not came to america, we should not

have been away from one and other, though now it can not be helped. I think for my part that it would have been a great deal better if the white people had not found it out. Let the (others) have it for themselves, for it was made for them. I have got a little of my grammar; sometimes I get three pages and sometimes but one. I do not sifer any at all. Mamma Peggy and Jacky are all very well, and I am to. — I still remain your most Affectionate Son,

"WILLIAM HAZLITT.

"The Rev. Mr. HAZLITT, London.
"To the care of Mr. DAVID LEWIS."

CHAPTER II

THE elder Hazlitt had spent the eight months between
his own return home and that of his family in London
in the house of Mr. David Lewis, a member of a Maidstone family, to whom the Hazlitts were indebted for
much of that kindness which, when it happens to be
accompanied by delicacy, has often sweetened the hard
lot of those who insist upon thinking. for themselves
in things spiritual. These hospitable folk received
the whole family on its arrival from Portsmouth, and
entertained it for some weeks, until a lodging was
taken at Walworth near the once-celebrated Montpelier Tea Gardens. To this cheerful resort his
friendly and companionable father used to take for a
ramble the future essayist, who has painted for us the
very place.

"When I was quite a boy, my father used to take
me to the Montpelier Tea-gardens at Walworth. Do
I go there now? No: the place is deserted, and its
borders and its beds o'erturned. Is there, then,
nothing that can

'Bring back the hour
Of glory in the grass, of splendour in the flower'?

Oh yes. I unlock the casket of memory, and draw
back the warders of the brain; and there this scene

17

of my infant wanderings still lives unfaded, or with
fresher dyes. A new sense comes upon me, as in a
dream; a richer perfume, brighter colours start out;
my eyes dazzle; my heart heaves with its new load of
bliss, and I am a child again. My sensations are all
glossy, spruce, voluptuous, and fine; they wear a
candied coat, and are in holiday trim. I see the beds
of larkspur with purple eyes; tall hollyhocks, red and
yellow; the brown sunflowers, caked in gold, with
bees buzzing round them; wildernesses of pinks and
hot-glowing peonies; poppies run to seed; the sugared
lily and faint mignonette, all ranged in order, and
as thick as they can grow; the box-tree borders; the
gravel-walks, the painted alcove, the confectionery,
the clotted cream; — I think I see them now with
sparkling looks, or have they vanished while I have
been writing this description of them? No matter;
they will return again when I least think of them.
All that I have observed since, of flowers and plants,
and grass-plots, and of suburb delights, seems, to me,
borrowed from 'that first garden of my innocence,'
to be slips and scions stolen from that bed of memory."[1]

Another lodging in Percy Street soon received them,
and here they stayed through the whole autumn of
1787, receiving a visit of a month's duration from old
Mrs. Loftus already mentioned, who, though then
eighty-four, had still fourteen years to live. John
Hazlitt obtained admission into the studios of the
great Sir Joshua, and pursued his art with the utmost
zest. Margaret the diarist had also a strong artistic

---

[1] 'Why distant objects please.' — *Table-Talk.*

bent; and whenever she could manage it, William and she would flatten their noses against the windows of the print shops in Pall Mall, and great was her rapture when her father actually took her into Boydell's Gallery and bought a print — "The Fish-stealers by Moonlight."

The wanderings of the elder Hazlitt were now, however, nearly at an end. In the winter of 1787 he accepted the charge of a small congregation at Wem, in Shropshire, and at Wem he remained for more than a quarter of a century.

Wem is a well-known name to all Hazlitt's readers. Wem, in Shropshire, and Winterslow Hutt, by Salisbury Plain, were two places of joy in his self-tormenting, self-rejoicing life; and so well has he succeeded in infecting them with his own delight, that it is hard to be dull at Wem or indifferent at Winterslow.

At Wem Hazlitt remained, with but few periods of absence, from his tenth to his twenty-second year, from 1788 to 1802 — a good slice out of life, and when impressions cut deepest, and indeed, like the mercy of God, endure for ever. Hazlitt, like Macaulay, was a most tenacious person, though the tenacity of the latter had a Whiggish cast differentiating it from the tenacity of the born sentimentalist. "If I see a row of cabbage-plants or of peas or beans coming up, I immediately think of those which I used so carefully to water of an evening at Wem when my day's task was done, and of the pain with which I saw them droop and hang down their leaves in the morning's sun." Again, "I never see a child's kite but it seems to pull at my heart."

At Wem William became in a very real sense his

father's pupil, though he must also have attended a day school; for in a long letter written to his brother from Wem in March 1788, he tells John that he goes to school at nine every morning, and after three of the boys have read from the Bible, he and two others (is this an early Conscience Clause protecting the young Dissenter?) showed their exercises. After this odd distinction, the whole class read Enfield's *Speaker*. At spelling Hazlitt asserts he was almost always first. As for the boys, some he declares are so sulky that they won't play, and others are quarrelsome because they cannot learn, and are fit only for fighting like stupid dogs and cats. " I can jump four yards at a running jump and two at a standing jump. I intend to try you at this when you come down."

This same letter reveals a taste both for drawing and reading. " You want to know what I do: I am a busybody, and do many silly things. I drew eyes and noses till about a fortnight ago. I have drawn a little boy since, a man's face, and a little boy's front-face taken from a bust. Next Monday I shall begin to read Ovid's *Metamorphoses* and *Eutropius*. I shall like to know all the Latin and Greek I can. I want to learn how to measure the stars. I shall not, I suppose, paint the worse for knowing everything else." The letter concludes thus: "I don't want your old clothes. I shall go to dancing this month. This is all I can say. — I am, your affectionate brother, WILLIAM HAZLITT."

Margaret's account of him at this time is as follows: —

" The first six years subsequent to our settlement at Wem he devoted to study, and under his father's guidance he

made a rapid progress. He was at this time the most
active, lively, and happiest of boys; his time divided between his studies and his childish sports passed smoothly
on. Beloved by all for his amiable temper and manners,
pleasing above his years, the delight and pride of his own
family."

The slouch in the gait and the hand fumbling for
the hidden dagger were things of another birth, even
if they were not, like the pimples with which Professor
Wilson's young men in *Blackwood* bespread Hazlitt's
face, altogether the offspring of lurid fancy.

During these years at Wem the character and attitude of mind towards both spiritual and political
affairs of the elder Hazlitt made a great impression on
the imagination of the son. There was sympathy
between them. The original bent of the younger
Hazlitt's mind was towards metaphysical reflection,
nor had he any inborn distaste for theology, or even to
going to chapel twice on Sundays. In the politics of
the day he naturally took a keen interest; and could,
when ten years old, give the arguments for the Repeal
of the Test and Corporation Acts as well as any living
man in Parliament or pothouse. The father rejoiced
exceedingly at this youthful prowess, and with "for-
ward-reaching thoughts" already saw the boy he loved
expounding from the pulpit with fiery eloquence and
convincing force the principles of true religion, the
charm of a holy life, and the rights of man. "My
father," said Hazlitt, "would far sooner I had preached
a good sermon than painted a Rembrandt"; and this,
not because the elder Hazlitt was blind to the sur-
passing merit of Rembrandt, but because to him a
sermon belonged to the Life Eternal.

The study at Wem contained much massy divinity.
Caryl's *Commentaries on Job*, in folio volumes, was
amongst the lighter reading which greatly exercised
the young Hazlitt's imagination, even though its
perusal did not occupy much of his time. "It is
delightful to repose on the Wisdom of the Ancients;
to travel out of one's self into the Chaldee, Hebrew,
and Egyptian characters; to have the palm-trees
waving mystically in the margin of the page, and the
camels moving slowly on in the distance of three
thousand years." His father and his father's books
were always very near Hazlitt's heart; and though the
sermons he preached were not after his father's fashion, nevertheless the father was sometimes the text;
and whenever this was the case, the discourse glows
with an eloquence not surpassed by Taylor or Bossuet.
No biographer of Hazlitt can dispense with long quotation, although how this biographer will have the
courage to resume the pen when his next quotation
comes to an end he cannot think.

"A Dissenting minister is a character not so easily to be
dispensed with and whose place cannot be well supplied. It
is a pity that this character has worn itself out; that that
pulse of thought and feeling has ceased almost to beat in the
heart of a nation, who, if not remarkable for sincerity and
plain downright well-meaning, are remarkable for nothing.
But we have known some such, in happier days, who had
been brought up and lived from youth to age in the one constant belief of God and of his Christ, and who thought all
other things but dross compared with the glory hereafter to
be revealed. Their youthful hopes and vanity had been
mortified in them, even in their boyish days, by the neglect
and supercilious regards of the world; and they turned to
look into their own minds for something else to build their

hopes and confidence upon. They were true priests. They
set up an image in their own minds — it was truth; they worshipped an idol there — it was justice. They looked on man
as their brother, and only bowed the knee to the Highest.
Separate from the world, they walked humbly with their
God, and lived in thought with those who had borne testimony of a good conscience, with the spirits of just men in all
ages. They saw Moses when he slew the Egyptian, and the
prophets who overturned the brazen images, and those who
were stoned and sawn asunder. They were with Daniel in the
lions' den, and with the three children who passed through the
fiery furnace — Meshach, Shadrach, and Abed-nego; they did
not crucify Christ twice over, or deny Him in their hearts,
with St. Peter; the *Book of Martyrs* was open to them; they
read the story of William Tell, of John Huss, and Jerome of
Prague, and the old one-eyed Zisca; they had Neale's *History
of the Puritans* by heart, and Calamy's *Account of the Two
Thousand Ejected Ministers*, and gave it to their children to
read, with the pictures of the polemical Baxter, the silver-
tongued Bates, the mild-looking Calamy, and old honest
Howe; they believed in Lardner's *Credibility of the Gospel
History;* they were deep read in the works of *Fratres Poloni*,
Pripscovius, Crellius, Cracovius, who sought out truth in texts
of Scripture, and grew blind over Hebrew points; their aspiration after liberty was a sigh uttered from the towers, ' time-
rent,' of the Holy Inquisition; and their zeal for religious
toleration was kindled at the fires of Smithfield. Their
sympathy was not with the oppressors, but the oppressed.
They cherished in their thoughts — and wished to transmit
to their posterity — those rights and privileges for asserting
which their ancestors had bled on scaffolds, or had pined in
dungeons, or in foreign climes. Their creed, too, was 'Glory
to God, peace on earth, goodwill to man.' This creed, since
profaned and rendered vile, they kept fast through good
report and evil report. This belief they had, that looks at
something out of itself, fixed as the stars, deep as the firma-
ment; that makes of its own heart an altar to truth, a place
of worship for what is right, at which it does reverence with
praise and prayer like a holy thing, apart and content; that

feels that the greatest Being in the universe is always near it ; and that all things work together for the good of His creatures, under His guiding hand.   This covenant they kept, as the stars keep their courses ; this principle they stuck by, for want of knowing better, as it sticks by them to the last.   It grew with their growth, it does not wither in their decay.   It lives when the almond-tree flourishes, and is not bowed down with the tottering knees.   It glimmers with the last feeble eyesight, smiles in the faded cheek like infancy, and lights a path before them to the grave ! " [1]

The last words of this magnificent utterance and large discourse were written in January 1818, and reprinted in the following year.   The old man who inspired the whole passage died in July 1820, aged eighty-four.

It would be a mistake to suppose from the filial pride and fervent language of Hazlitt that he was in the least inclined to become "a Rational Dissenter." It is only necessary to read his philosophical essay " On the Tendency of Sects " in the *Round Table* (1817) to be disabused of such a notion.   Politically, he admired the fidelity of the old Nonconformists to their unpopular opinions, and their " abstract attachment" to their principles ; but philosophically he was as much alive as the late Dr. Martineau to the crudity of the Unitarian controversy, and to the ill consequences apt to flow from the habit of objecting to everything.   Hazlitt was never a true Dissenter any more than he was ever a true Democrat.

In 1790, when entering upon his thirteenth year, Hazlitt paid a long visit to some friends of his father's in Liverpool, called Tracy, good Unitarians, who took

[1] 'On Court Influence.' — *Political Essays.*

him to hear Mr. Yates on Sundays, and let him share
the French lessons of a little Miss Tracy. Here he
read *Télémaque*, and began to qualify himself for that
sensuous enjoyment of Rousseau which was to play such
a part in his life. His letters home are most amusing.
A few extracts must serve : —

"Saturday afternoon I and George, with Miss Avis, went
to a Mrs. Barton's, who appeared to be an unhospitable
English prim 'lady,' if such she may be called. She asked
us, as if she were afraid we should accept it, if we would
stay to tea. And at the other English person's, for I am
sure she belongs to no other country than to England, I got
such a surfeit of their ceremonial unsociality, that I could
not help wishing myself in America. I had rather people
would tell one to go out of the house than ask one to stay,
and, at the same time, be trembling all over for fear one
should take a slice of meat, or a dish of tea, with them.
Such as these require an Horace or a Shakespeare to describe
them. I have not yet learned the gamut perfectly, but I
would have done it if I could. I spent a very agreeable day
yesterday, as I read 160 pages of Priestley, and heard two
good sermons ; the best of which, in my opinion, was
Mr. Lewin's, and the other Mr. Smith's. They both belong
to Benn's Gardens Chapel."

"I do not converse in French ; but I and Miss Tracy have
a book, something like a vocabulary, where we get the mean-
ings of words. Miss Tracy never does accompts, but I take
an hour or two every other day. I will follow your Greek
precept. Give my best love to mamma, and tell her I shall
write to her next time, and hope she will write to me in
answer to it."

His father replies with mild philosophy —

"Your conversation upon the Test Act did you honour.
If we only think justly, we shall always easily foil all the
advocates of tyranny. The inhospitable ladies whom you
mention were, perhaps, treated by you with too great severity.

We know not how people may be circumstanced at a particular moment, whose disposition is generally friendly. They may, then, happen to pass under a cloud, which unfits them for social intercourse. We must see them more than once or twice to be able to form a tolerable judgment of their characters. There are but few, like Mrs. Tracy, who can always appear what they really are. I do not say, however, that the English ladies whom you mention are not exactly as you described them. I only wish to caution you against forming too hasty a judgment of characters who can seldom be known at a single interview. I wish you, if you can, to become master of the gamut while you are there. I am glad that you have made so great a progress in French, and that you are so very anxious to hear Mr. Clegg's lectures. It is a pity that you cannot have another month at the French, etc. But, as matters are, I hope you will be soon able to master that language. I am glad that you employed the last Sunday so well, and that the employment afforded you so much satisfaction. Nothing else can truly satisfy us but the acquisition of knowledge and virtue. May these blessings be yours more and more every day!"

At Liverpool Hazlitt went to his first play.

"On Friday I went to the play with Mr. Corbett, at whose house I dined and drank tea. The play was *Love in Many Masks*, and the farce *No Song, No Supper*. It was very entertaining, and was performed by some of the best players in London, as, for instance, Kemble, Suett, Dignum, the famous singer, Mrs. Williams, Miss Hagley, Miss Romanzini, and others. Suett, who acted in the character of 'Ned Blunt,' was enough to make any one laugh though he stood still; and Kemble acted admirably as an officer. Mr. Dignum sang beautifully, and Miss Hagley acted the country girl with much exactness. Mr. Corbett says he will take us to another play before we go. So much for last week." [1]

[1] "I met Dignum (the singer) in the street the other day; he was humming a tune, and his eye though quenched was smiling.

He is also taken for the first time in his life to the Established Church, and thinks little of it.

"On Sunday, after I had come from meeting, I went, but not willingly, to Mrs. Sydebotham's to dinner. In the afternoon we went to church, for the first time I ever was in one, and I do not care if I should never go into one again. The clergyman, after he had gabbled over half-a-dozen prayers, began his sermon, the text of which was as follows :— Zechariah, 3rd chapter, 2nd verse, latter part — 'Is not this a brand plucked out of the fire ? ' If a person had come in five minutes after he began, he would have thought that he had taken his text out of Joshua. In short, his sermon had neither head nor tail. I was sorry that so much time should be thrown away upon nonsense. I often wished I was hearing Mr. Yates ; but I shall see I do not go to church again in a hurry."

But he remains loyal to the Throne. "I cannot play any tune upon the harpsichord but 'God save the King.'" Charles Lamb never managed even to hum it.

He adds a postscript, "I shall have *satis pecuniæ, dum tu habeas opportunitatem mittendi aliquam partem mihi.*"

His father, who was too good a Christian not to be fine-mannered, sends him careful directions how to deport himself on his departure from the Tracys, bidding him be careful to leave none of his things behind him, lest Mrs. Tracy should have the trouble of send-

I could scarcely forbear going up to speak to him. Why so? I had seen him in the year 1792 (? 1790) (the first time I was ever at a play (with Suett and Miss Romanzini and some others in *No Song, No Supper ;* and ever since, that bright vision of my childhood has played round my fancy with unabated, vivid delight."— See *The New School of Reform*, in the *Plain Speaker* (1826).

ing them after him, and reminding him after meeting
to seek Mr. Yates in his vestry and say good-bye, and
also to call on his friends who had showed him any
attention.

"But what must you say to Mrs. Tracy?   I leave that
entirely to yourself.   But present her with your mamma's
respects and mine, and our sincere thanks, and tell her that
we wish to see her again, and that we also hope for this
pleasure with all the young ladies, and all of them quite
happy."

He adds, else he had not been a Unitarian Parson
Adams, "My sermons will soon be printed. I shall
embrace the first opportunity of sending Mrs. Tracy a
copy."

If in later life Hazlitt's manners left much to be
desired, as seems to have been the case, it was not the
Dissenting minister's fault.

It was a grave bringing up for a man whose writings
are chiefly remarkable for the fierce enjoyment they
exhibit for all brave, sublunary things.

"To see the golden sun, the azure sky, the outstretched
ocean ; to walk upon the green earth, and to be lord of a
thousand creatures ; to look down yawning precipices, or over
distant sunny vales ; to see the world spread out under one's
feet on a map ; to bring the stars near ; to view the smallest
insects through a microscope ; to read history, and consider
the revolutions of empire and the successions of generations ;
to hear of the glory of Tyre, of Sidon, of Babylon, and of
Susa, and to say all these were before me and are now nothing ; to say I exist in such a point of time, and in such a
point of space ; to be a spectator and a part of its ever-
moving scene ; to witness the change of season, of spring
and autumn, of winter and summer ; to feel hot and cold,
pleasure and pain, beauty and deformity, right and wrong ;

to be sensible to the accidents of nature ; to consider the mighty world of eye and ear ; to listen to the stockdove's notes amid the forest deep ; to journey over moor and mountain ; to hear the midnight sainted choir ; to visit lighted halls, or the cathedral's gloom, or sit in crowded theatres and see life itself mocked ; to study the works of art, and refine the sense of beauty to agony ; to worship fame, and to dream of immortality ; to look upon the Vatican and to read Shakespeare ; to gather up the wisdom of the ancients and to pry into the future ; to listen to the trump of war, the shout of victory ; to question history as to the movements of the human heart ; to seek for truth ; to plead the cause of humanity ; to overlook the world as if time and nature poured their treasures at our feet — to be and to do all this, and then in a moment to be nothing." [1]

This is the familiar strain of the most eloquent of English essayists, but in the beginning of things Hazlitt was slow of speech and sluggish in fancy — the bent of his mind being, as already remarked, speculative and reflective. " When I was about fourteen," he writes, " in consequence of a dispute one day after meeting between my father and an old lady of the congregation respecting the repeal of the Corporation and Test Acts and the limits of religious toleration, I set about forming in my head (the first time I ever attempted to think) the following system of political rights and general jurisprudence." He began by trying to define what a right was, and then asked, shrewdly enough, What is law ? What the real ground of Civil Government ? Whence, he asked, has the community the right to coerce any of its members ? Hobbes he had not heard of, and probably he was indebted to Priestley, one of the gods of his

---

[1] ' On the Feeling of Immortality in Youth.'— *Winterslow*.

father's idolatry, for much assistance as he pursued his "dim and perilous way." Four corollaries follow in due order, leading up to the satisfactory conclusion that there are four things a man may call his own—his person, his actions, his property, and his opinions. On each of these, however, there is a good deal to be said by way of definition, limitation, and necessary qualification; and we soon find Hazlitt discussing such a detail as the law against Nuisances, and enlivening the disquisition with a pleasant tale of the rector of Wem, who having, as befitted a Canonist, a quarrel with the local attorney, whose name was Wickstead, used to collect in his garden a heap of rubbish and weeds; and when the wind was in the right quarter, would observe significantly to his gardener, "It is a fine Wickstead wind to-day," and thereupon a match was applied.

It is not to be supposed that the whole of the sensible discourse, now to be found printed in the *Literary Remains* (1836), was composed in Hazlitt's fourteenth year. By no means, but for some time, until indeed he began to ponder for another period of years his darling discovery in metaphysics, he seems to have kept turning the subject over and over in his mind, carrying it with him to Hackney Theological College, to which seminary of unorthodox religion he proceeded in that year of dread, 1793, with the intent on his father's side, at all events, of being turned into a Unitarian divine.

From his letters home we obtain some knowledge of the course of study there pursued. Hazlitt's classical tutor lectured on Sophocles one week, and Quintilian the next, also on Greek Grammar and Antiquities.

Hazlitt tells his father that he can translate better than any of his fellow collegers.   Dr. Rees taught mathematics, and Dr. Price, I know not what — perhaps pastoral theology.   Philosophy was represented by the interesting name of Hartley, then the pet philosopher of Unitarians.   Divinity fared badly with the inevitable Belsham.   A tincture of Hebrew was imparted, and there was a class in logic.   Amidst these time-honoured pursuits it is odd to find shorthand being taught.   Altogether, as things went in England in 1793, Hackney College was a better *Studium Generale* than either Oxford or Cambridge at the same date.   Of what sort was the teaching I cannot say.

The letters home contain a moving account how Hazlitt succeeded in palming off upon his tutor the essay " On the Political State of Man," and in forcing that reluctant professor to accept it in lieu of the theme actually set.   " My chief reason," he writes to his father, who had urged the abandonment of these speculations, "for wishing to continue my observations, is that by having a particular system of politics I shall be better able to judge of the truth or falsehood of any principle which I hear or read, and of the justice or the contrary of any political transactions. Moreover, by comparing my own system with those of others, and with particular facts, I shall have it in my power to correct and improve it continually. . . . Besides, so far is my studying the subject from making me gloomy or low-spirited, I am never so perfectly easy as when I am or have been studying it."

Here we strike across the true Hazlitt vein — " my own system."   " I am not to be browbeat or wheedled out of any of my settled convictions.   Opinion to opinion I will face any man. Kings love power, misers gold, women flattery, poets reputation — and philosophers truth when they can find it. If to 'be wise were to be obstinate,' I might set up for as great a philosopher as the best of them, for some of my conclusions are as fixed and as incorrigible to proof as need be." [1] If Hazlitt had been a Whig, he could not have said more.

In the letter to his father just quoted there is a reference to gloom and low spirits, banished by agreeable system-making. There are many allusions at this time to " repeated disappointments," "long dejection," and other symptoms of boyish melancholy, and it is plain that Hackney College was not congenial.

Philosophy and speculation had their rival even at Hackney, for once a fortnight Hazlitt was allowed to visit his brother John, whose studio was then in Longacre, and spend a Sunday with him. No need to dwell on the influence of these fortnightly meetings. The brothers were greatly attached to one another. John was an enthusiast both for his Art and for the Revolution; and as William from boyhood seems to have fancied himself a painter, the wonder is that on leaving Hackney, as he did after little more than a year's experience of it, he did not at once fling himself headlong into a course of study and practice of those Fine Arts always dear to him.

He did nothing of this kind; but some time, probably in 1794, went back to his father's house at Wem, and there remained, doing what respectable people call "nothing" for eight years. His father, whose ex-

---

[1] 'On Consistency of Opinion.' — *Winterslow.*

pectations had been disappointed, probably found this inactivity the easier to bear, as it enabled him still to nurse the hope that his son might yet be reconciled to Priestley and Belsham, and become a preacher of rational religion and true holiness.

These eight years (1794–1802) at Wem were important years in Hazlitt's life as well as in the history of Europe. Few young men have so long and so quiet a time to brood over their thoughts, to nurse their fancies, and, it well may be, to feed their delusions. For a sentimentalist in grain a severer discipline, a more rigorous course of reading, would have been better. Both Hazlitt and his great contemporary Landor cultivated their self-will at too great a pace during these years.[1]

It is never safe to place much reliance upon the confessions of a man whose genius lies in picturesque expression. Hazlitt tells us that during these eight years he could do nothing. "I could not write a line, I could not draw a stroke, I was brutish. In words, in looks, in deeds, I was no better than a changeling." Again he says, "I was at that time dumb, inarticulate, helpless like a worm by the wayside, crushed, bleeding, lifeless." In 1796 he chanced to take up, on one of his many rambles, or perhaps in Shrewsbury, a number of the *St. James's Chronicle*, which contained a long extract from Burke's "Letter to a Noble Lord." It was the first time Hazlitt had read a line of Burke's. Hazlitt is famous for his "first times," and this was one of them. It was at once supreme delight and

[1] It is traditionally reported that Hazlitt never read a book through after he was thirty. Much the same is said of Dr. Johnson.

horrid pain.   Delight to disport himself on those
crested waves, to be borne along by their overwhelm-
ing strength, to glory in their froth and fume — pain
to think of himself "vainly trying year after year to
write a single essay, nay, a single page, a sentence;
and when to be able to convey the slightest conception
of my meaning to others in words was the height of
an almost hopeless ambition."

To wrestle with native infirmities, to strive to pierce
through the dull clay in which most of us are kneaded,
is hard labour, but when health and spirits are unim-
paired it is healthy toil; and side by side with the
doleful passages from which I have quoted, other
passages are to be found in Hazlitt's writings, in which
he declares these same years of bitter strife to be the
happiest years of all.   "I had at this time, simple as
I seemed, many resources.   I could in some sort 'play
at bowls with the sun and moon,' or at any rate there
was no question in metaphysics I could not bandy to
and fro for twenty, thirty, forty miles of the great
North Road, and at it again the next day as fresh as
ever.   I soon get tired of this now, and wonder how
I managed formerly.   I knew *Tom Jones* by heart,
and was deep in *Peregrine Pickle ;* I was intimately
acquainted with all the heroes and heroines of Richardson's romances, and could turn from one to other as
I pleased."   For novels and plays there never was
such a reader, nor was he over-critical — the most
stilted of heroines, the palest of sentimental shadows,
could always be relied upon to trundle her hoop into
Hazlitt's heart.   These things were more to him than
actual events, and Shrewsbury was dearer to him
because Farquhar had made it the scene of *The
Recruiting Officer.*

To such a mind, so situated, and in the years 1796 and onwards, Rousseau was manna from heaven — nectar from Olympus. "Many a dainty repast have I made of the *New Eloïse;* the description of the kiss, the excursion on the water, the letter of St. Preux recalling the time of their first loves, and the account of Julia's death, — these I read over and over again with unspeakable delight and wonder." "I spent two whole years in reading the *Confessions* and the *New Eloïse*, and (gentle reader, it was when I was young) in shedding tears over them

> 'As fast as the Arabian trees
> Their medicinal gums.'

They were the happiest years of my life."

When Hazlitt was not wrestling with a sluggish pen or revelling in Rousseau, he was walking. He scoured the country in all directions, visiting Burleigh House to see the pictures (notably a Rembrandt), going on a pilgrimage to Wisbeach to visit the farmhouse where his mother was born, so that he might lean upon the gate she leant against when, as a child of ten, she stood gazing at the setting sun. Occasional visits he paid to his brother John in London, where he met the Godwins, Holcroft, and on one occasion Mrs. Wollstonecraft.

One friend he made at this time of his life, to whom on his literary side he owed much — Joseph Fawcett, a retired Unitarian minister, not without fame in his own day and circle. Fawcett is mentioned as living both at Hedgegrove in Hertfordshire and Walthamstow. Hazlitt delighted in his society, and gained much from his conversation. Of him Haz-

litt writes : " He was almost the first literary acquaintance I ever made, and I think the most candid and
unsophisticated. He had a masterly perception of
all styles and of every kind and degree of excellence, sublime or beautiful, from Milton's *Paradise
Lost* to Shenstone's *Pastoral Ballad*, from Butler's
Analogy to *Humphrey Clinker*. If you had a favourite author, he had read him too, and knew all the best
morsels, the subtile traits, the capital touches. ' So
you like Sterne ? ' ' Yes, to be sure,' he would say,
' I should deserve to be hanged if I did not.' His repeating some parts of Comus with his fine, deep, mel-
low-toned voice, particularly the lines, ' I have heard
my mother Circe with the sirens three,' etc., and the
enthusiastic comments he made afterwards were a
feast to the ear and to the soul. He read the poetry
of Milton with the same fervour and spirit of devotion that I have since heard others read their own.
' That is the most delicious feeling of all,' I have heard
him exclaim, ' to like what is excellent, no matter whose
it is.' In this respect he practised what he preached.
He was incapable of harbouring a sinister motive, and
judged only from what he felt. There was no flaw or
mist in the clear mirror of his mind. He was as open
to impressions as he was strenuous in maintaining
them. He did not care a rush whether a writer was
old or new in prose or in verse. ' What he wanted,'
he said, ' was something to make him think.' Most
men's minds are to me like musical instruments out
of tune. Touch a particular key, and it jars and
makes harsh discord with your own. They like *Gil
Blas*, but can see nothing to laugh at in *Don Quixote;*
they adore Richardson, but are disgusted with Field-

ing. Fawcett had a taste accommodated to all these.
He was not exceptious. He gave a cordial welcome
to all sorts, provided they were the best in their kind.
He was not fond of counterfeits or duplicates."

Hazlitt's devotion to Fawcett both in life and after
death is a little marred by the too great pleasure he
takes in contrasting his early friend's generous recognition of good wherever he could find it with Wordsworth's steady reluctance to see good in anything but
himself. But we must certainly rank Joseph Fawcett
as among the good fortunes of our critic that is to be.

In 1798, when Hazlitt was nearly twenty years old,
and still "doing nothing" in his father's house, something happened which put a period to his boyhood and
gave him understanding and language — he met Coleridge, whose talk was "far above singing," and whose
words might create a soul "under the ribs of death."
How this meeting came about will be told next in language which, however familiar, can never grow stale,
so full is it of humour, insight, and philosophy.

CHAPTER III

COLERIDGE

COLERIDGE came to Shrewsbury in January 1798, with some notion of succeeding a Mr. Rowe in the charge of the Unitarian chapel, then, and still, to be found in that pleasant town. His fame in 1798 might have rested, not insecurely, on his published poems, which already included " The Monody to Chatterton " and the " Ode on the Departing Year "; but to the Unitarians of Shrewsbury he was probably only known for his vigorous efforts, so amusingly recorded by him, to procure subscribers for the *Watchman*, " preaching by the way in a blue coat and white waistcoat."

Coleridge arrived in Shrewsbury by coach very late on Saturday night, much to the relief of Mr. Rowe, who was waiting for his substitute with the anxiety of a divine who had prepared no sermon for the morrow. Mr. Rowe, on seeing Coleridge for the first time, found it hard to believe that the round-faced man in a shooting jacket was his successor — nor was he.

At Shrewsbury, Coleridge remained three weeks — preaching, so he tells us, with much acceptance to a small congregation, which contained at least one member shrewd enough to remark that he would sooner hear Coleridge talk than preach.

The news of this approaching visit to Shrewsbury

reached Wem, and so stirred the heart of the younger
Hazlitt, who had heard from the Godwins about the
greatness of Coleridge, that he could not wait for the
promised visit of the great man to his father's house,
but he must needs walk in to Shrewsbury, ten miles
there and as many back, to hear him preach. The
rest must follow in Hazlitt's own words : —

" It was in January 1798 that I rose one morning before
daylight to walk ten miles in the mud to hear this celebrated
person preach.   Never, the longest day I have to live, shall
I have such another walk as this cold, raw, comfortless one,
in the winter of the year 1798.   *Il y a des impressions que
ni le tems ni les circonstances peuvent effacer.   Dussé-je
vivre des siècles entiers, le doux tems de ma jeunesse ne peut
renaître pour moi, ni s'effacer jamais dans ma mémoire.*
When I got there the organ was playing the 100th Psalm ;
and when it was done, Mr. Coleridge rose and gave out his
text, ' And he went up into the mountain to pray, HIMSELF,
ALONE.'   As he gave out this text his voice 'rose like a
stream of rich distilled perfumes ' ; and when he came to
the two last words, which he pronounced loud, deep, and
distinct, it seemed to me, who was then young, as if the
sounds had echoed from the bottom of the human heart, and
as if that prayer might have floated in solemn silence through
the universe.   The idea of St. John came into my mind, ' of
one crying in the wilderness, who had his loins girt about,
and whose food was locusts and wild honey.'   The preacher
then launched into his subject, like an eagle dallying with
the wind.   The sermon was upon Peace and War ; upon
Church and State — not their alliance, but their separation
— on the Spirit of the World and the Spirit of Christianity,
not as the same, but as opposed to one another.   He talked
of those who had ' inscribed the cross of Christ on banners
dripping with human gore.'   He made a poetical and pastoral excursion ; and to show the fatal effects of war, drew
a striking contrast between the simple shepherd boy, driving
his team afield, or sitting under the hawthorn, piping to his

flock, 'as though he should never be old,' and the same poor country lad, crimped, kidnapped, brought into town, made drunk at an alehouse, turned into a wretched drummer-boy, with his hair sticking on end with powder and pomatum, a long cue at his back, and tricked out in the loathsome finery of the profession of blood.

　　'Such were the notes our once-loved poet sung.'

And for myself, I could not have been more delighted if I had heard the music of the spheres. Poetry and Philosophy had met together, Truth and Genius had embraced, under the eye and with the sanction of Religion. This was even beyond my hopes. I returned home well satisfied. The sun that was still labouring pale and wan through the sky, obscured by thick mists, seemed an emblem of the *good cause ;* and the cold dank drops of dew, that hung half melted on the beard of the thistle, had something genial and refreshing in them ; for there was a spirit of hope and youth in all nature that turned everything into good.

" On the Tuesday following the half-inspired speaker came. I was called down into the room where he was, and went half hoping, half afraid. He received me very graciously, and I listened for a long time without uttering a word. I did not suffer in his opinion by my silence. 'For those two hours,' he afterwards was pleased to say, ' he was conversing with William Hazlitt's forehead ! ' [1] His appearance was different from what I had anticipated from seeing him before. At a distance, and in the dim light of the chapel, there was to me a strange wildness in his aspect, a dusky obscurity, and I thought him pitted with the smallpox. His complexion was at that time clear, and even bright —

　　' As are the children of yon azure sheen.'

His forehead was broad and high, light as if built of ivory, with large projecting eyebrows, and his eyes rolling beneath

　　[1] If Haydon is to be believed, Hazlitt never forgot his compliment to his forehead, which no doubt was almost as fine as the compliment.

them, like a sea with darkened lustre. 'A certain tender bloom his face o'erspread,' a purple tinge as we see it in the pale thoughtful complexions of the Spanish portrait-painters, Murillo and Velasquez. His mouth was gross, voluptuous, open, eloquent ; his chin good-humoured and round ; but his nose, the rudder of the face, the index of the will, was small, feeble, nothing — like what he has done. It might seem that the genius of his face as from a height surveyed and projected him (with sufficient capacity and huge aspiration) into the world unknown of thought and imagination, with nothing to support or guide his veering purpose, as if Columbus had launched his adventurous course for the New World in a scallop, without oars or compass. So at least I comment on it after the event. Coleridge in his person was rather above the common size, inclining to the corpulent, or, like Lord Hamlet, 'somewhat fat and pursy.' His hair (now, alas ! grey) was then black and glossy as the raven's, and fell in smooth masses over his forehead. This long pendulous hair is peculiar to enthusiasts, to those whose minds tend heavenward, and is traditionally inseparable (though of a different colour) from the pictures of Christ. It ought to belong, as a character, to all who preach *Christ crucified*, and Coleridge was at that time one of those !

" It was curious to observe the contrast between him and my father, who was a veteran in the cause, and then declining into the vale of years. He had been a poor Irish lad, carefully brought up by his parents, and sent to the University of Glasgow to prepare him for his future destination. It was his mother's proudest wish to see her son a Dissenting minister. So, if we look back to past generations (as far as eye can reach), we see the same hopes, fears, wishes, followed by the same disappointments, throbbing in the human heart ; and so we may see them (if we look forward) rising up for ever, and disappearing, like vapourish bubbles, in the human breast ! After being tossed about from congregation to congregation in the heats of the Unitarian controversy, and squabbles about the American war, he had been relegated to an obscure village, where he was to spend the last thirty years of his life, far from the only converse that he loved,

the talk about disputed texts of Scripture, and the cause
of civil and religious liberty. Here he passed his days,
repining, but resigned, in the study of the Bible and the
perusal of the commentators — huge folios, not easily got
through, one of which would outlast a winter! Why did
he pore on these from morn to night (with the exception of
a walk in the fields or a turn in the garden to gather broccoli
plants or kidney beans of his own rearing, with no small
degree of pride and pleasure)? Here were 'no figures nor
no fantasies,' neither poetry nor philosophy, nothing to dazzle,
nothing to excite modern curiosity; but to his lack-lustre
eyes there appeared, within the pages of the ponderous,
unwieldy, neglected tomes, the sacred name of JEHOVAH in
Hebrew capitals: pressed down by the weight of the style,
worn to the last fading thinness of the understanding, there
were glimpses, glimmering notions of the patriarchal wanderings, with palm-trees hovering in the horizon, and proces-
sions of camels at the distance of three thousand years;
there was Moses with the Burning Bush, the number of the
Twelve Tribes, types, shadows, glosses on the law and the
prophets; there were discussions (dull enough) on the age of
Methuselah, a mighty speculation; there were outlines, rude
guesses at the shape of Noah's Ark and of the riches of
Solomon's Temple; questions as to the date of the Creation,
predictions of the end of all things; the great lapses of time,
the strange mutations of the globe were unfolded with the
voluminous leaf, as it turned over; and though the soul
might slumber with an hieroglyphic veil of inscrutable
mysteries drawn over it, yet it was in a slumber ill exchanged for all the sharpened realities of sense, wit, fancy,
or reason. My father's life was comparatively a dream; but
it was a dream of infinity and eternity, of death, the resurrection, and a judgment to come!

"No two individuals were ever more unlike than were the
host and his guest. A poet was to my father a sort of non-
descript; yet whatever added grace to the Unitarian cause
was to him welcome. He could hardly have been more surprised or pleased if our visitor had worn wings. Indeed, his
thoughts had wings; and, as the silken sounds rustled round

our little wainscoted parlour, my father threw back his spectacles over his forehead, his white hairs mixing with its
sanguine hue ; and a smile of delight beamed across his
rugged cordial face to think that Truth had found a new
ally in Fancy ! Besides, Coleridge seemed to take considerable notice of me, and that of itself was enough. He talked
very familiarly, but agreeably, and glanced over a variety of
subjects. At dinner-time he grew more animated, and dilated
in a very edifying manner on Mary Wollstonecraft and Mackintosh. The last, he said, he considered (on my father's
speaking of his *Vindiciæ Gallicæ* as a capital performance)
as a clever scholastic man — a master of the topics — or as
the ready warehouseman of letters, who knew exactly where
to lay his hand on what he wanted, though the goods were
not his own. He thought him no match for Burke, either
in style or matter. Burke was a metaphysician, Mackintosh
a mere logician. Burke was an orator (almost a poet) who
reasoned in figures, because he had an eye for nature ; Mackintosh, on the other hand, was a rhetorician, who had only
an eye to commonplaces. On this I ventured to say that I
had always entertained a great opinion of Burke, and that
(as far as I could find) the speaking of him with contempt
might be made the test of a vulgar democratical mind. This
was the first observation I ever made to Coleridge, and he
said it was a very just and striking one. I remember the
leg of Welsh mutton and the turnips on the table that day
had the finest flavour imaginable. Coleridge added that
Mackintosh and Tom Wedgwood (of whom, however, he
spoke highly) had expressed a very indifferent opinion of
his friend Mr. Wordsworth, on which he remarked to them,
' He strides on so far before you, that he dwindles in the
distance ! ' Godwin had once boasted to him of having carried on an argument with Mackintosh for three hours with
dubious success ; Coleridge told him, ' If there had been a
man of genius in the room, he would have settled the question in five minutes.' He asked me if I had ever seen Mary
Wollstonecraft, and I said I had once for a few moments,
and that she seemed to me to turn off Godwin's objections
to something she advanced with quite a playful, easy air.

He replied that 'this was only one instance of the ascendancy which people of imagination exercised over those of mere intellect.' He did not rate Godwin very high. He complained in particular of the presumption of his attempting to establish the future immortality of man, 'without' (as he said) 'knowing what Death was or what Life was,' and the tone in which he pronounced these two words seemed to convey a complete image of both. I forget a great number of things, many more than I remember; but the day passed off pleasantly, and the next morning Mr. Coleridge was to return to Shrewsbury. When I came down to breakfast, I found that he had just received a letter from his friend, T. Wedgwood, making him an offer of £150 a year if he chose to waive his present pursuit and devote himself entirely to the study of poetry and philosophy. Coleridge seemed to make up his mind to close with this proposal in the act of tying on one of his shoes. It threw an additional damp on his departure. It took the wayward enthusiast quite from us and cast him into Deva's winding vales, or by the shores of old romance. Instead of living at ten miles' distance, of being the pastor of a Dissenting congregation at Shrewsbury, he was henceforth to inhabit the Hill of Parnassus, to be a shepherd on the Delectable Mountains. Alas! I knew not the way thither, and felt very little gratitude for Mr. Wedgwood's bounty. I was presently relieved from this dilemma; for Mr. Coleridge, asking for a pen and ink, and going to a table to write something on a bit of card, advanced towards me with undulating step, and giving me the precious document, said that that was his address, *Mr. Coleridge, Nether-Stowey, Somersetshire;* and that he should be glad to see me there in a few weeks' time, and, if I chose, would come half-way to meet me. I was not less surprised than the shepherd boy (this simile is to be found in *Cassandra*) when he sees a thunderbolt fall close at his feet. I stammered out my acknowledgments and acceptance of this offer (I thought Mr. Wedgwood's annuity a trifle to it) as well as I could; and this mighty business being settled, the poet preacher took leave, and I accompanied him six miles on the road. It was a fine morning in the middle of winter, and he talked the whole way. The scholar in Chaucer is described as going

'Sounding on his way.'

So Coleridge went on his. In digressing, in dilating, in pass-ing from subject to subject, he appeared to me to float in air, to slide on ice. He told me in confidence (going along) that he should have preached two sermons before he accepted the situation at Shrewsbury — one on Infant Baptism ; the other on the Lord's Supper, showing that he could not admin-ister either — which would have effectually disqualified him for the object in view. I observed that he continually crossed me on the way by shifting from one side of the footpath to the other. This struck me as an odd movement ; but I did not at that time connect it with any instability of purpose or involuntary change of principle, as I have done since. He seemed unable to keep on in a straight line. He spoke slightingly of Hume (whose 'Essay on Miracles,' he said, was stolen from an objection started in one of South's sermons — *Credat Judæus Apella !*). I was not very much pleased at this account of Hume ; for I had just been reading, with infinite relish, that completest of all metaphysical *choke-pears*, his 'Treatise on Human Nature,' to which the 'Essays,' in point of scholastic subtilty and close reasoning, are mere elegant trifling, light summer reading. Coleridge even denied the excellence of Hume's general style, which I think betrayed a want of taste or candour. He, however, made me amends by the manner in which he spoke of Berkeley. He dwelt particularly on his 'Essay on Vision' as a masterpiece of analytical reasoning. So it undoubtedly is. He was exceedingly angry with Dr. Johnson for striking the stone with his foot, in allusion to this author's Theory of Matter and Spirit, and saying, 'Thus I confute him, sir.' Coleridge drew a parallel (I don't know how he brought about the connection) between Bishop Berkeley and Tom Paine. He said the one was an instance of a subtle, the other of an acute mind, than which no two things could be more distinct. The one was a shopboy's quality, the other the characteristic of a philosopher. He considered Bishop Butler as a true philosopher, a profound

and conscientious thinker, a genuine reader of nature and of
his own mind.   He did not speak of his *Analogy*, but of his
Sermons at the Rolls' Chapel, of which I had never heard.
Coleridge somehow always contrived to prefer the *unknown*
to the *known*.   In this instance he was right.   The *Analogy*
is a tissue of sophistry, of wire-drawn, theological special-
pleading; the *Sermons* (with the Preface to them) are in a
fine vein of deep, matured reflection, a candid appeal to our
observation of human nature, without pedantry and without
bias.   I told Coleridge I had written a few remarks, and was
sometimes foolish enough to believe that I had made a discovery on the same subject (the *Natural Disinterestedness of
the Human Mind*), and I tried to explain my view of it to
Coleridge, who listened with great willingness, but I did not
succeed in making myself understood.   I sat down to the task
shortly afterwards for the twentieth time, got new pens and
paper, determined to make clear work of it, wrote a few
meagre sentences in the skeleton style of a mathematical
demonstration, stopped half-way down the second page; and,
after trying in vain to pump up any words, images, notions,
apprehensions, facts, or observations, from that gulf of
abstraction in which I had plunged myself for four or five
years preceding, gave up the attempt as labour in vain, and
shed tears of helpless despondency on the blank unfinished
paper.   I can write fast enough now.   Am I better than I
was then ?   Oh no !   One truth discovered, one pang of
regret at not being able to express it, is better than all the
fluency and flippancy in the world.   Would that I could go
back to what I then was !   Why can we not revive past times
as we can revisit old places ?   If I had the quaint muse of
Sir Philip Sidney to assist me, I would write a ' Sonnet to the
Road between Wem and Shrewsbury,' and immortalise every
step of it by some fond enigmatical conceit.   I would swear
that the very milestones had ears, and that Harmer Hill
stooped with all its pines to listen to a poet as he passed !
I remember but one other topic of discourse in this walk.
He mentioned Paley, praised the naturalness and clearness of
his style, but condemned his sentiments, thought him a mere
time-serving casuist, and said that the fact of his work on

Moral and Political Philosophy being made a textbook in
our universities was a disgrace to the national character. We
parted at the six-mile stone ; and I returned homeward,
pensive but much pleased. I had met with unexpected notice
from a person whom I believed to have been prejudiced
against me. ' Kind and affable to me had been his condescension, and should be honoured ever with suitable regard.'
He was the first poet I had known, and he certainly answered
to that inspired name. I had heard a great deal of his powers
of conversation, and was not disappointed.

"On my way back, I had a sound in my ears — it was
the voice of Fancy ; I had a light before me — it was the
face of Poetry. The one still lingers there, the other has not
quitted my side ! Coleridge, in truth, met me half-way on the
ground of philosophy, or I should have not been won over to his
imaginative creed. I had an uneasy, pleasurable sensation
all the time, till I was to visit him. During those months
the chill breath of winter gave me a welcoming ; the vernal
air was balm and inspiration to me. The golden sunsets,
the silver star of evening, lighted me on my way to new
hopes and prospects. *I was to visit Coleridge in the spring.*
This circumstance was never absent from my thoughts,
and mingled with all my feelings. I wrote to him at the
time proposed, and received an answer postponing my intended visit for a week or two, but very cordially urging me
to complete my promise then. This delay did not damp,
but rather increased, my ardour. In the meantime, I went
to Llangollen Vale, by way of initiating myself in the
mysteries of natural scenery ; and I must say I was en-
chanted with it. I had been reading Coleridge's description of England, in his fine ' Ode on the Departing Year,'
and I applied it, *con amore,* to the objects before me.
That valley was to me (in a manner) the cradle of a new
existence ; in the river that winds through it my spirit was
baptized in the waters of Helicon !

"I returned home, and soon after set out on my journey
with unworn heart and untired feet. My way lay through
Worcester and Gloucester, and by Upton, where I thought
of Tom Jones and the adventure of the muff. I remember

getting completely wet through one day, and stopping at an
inn (I think it was at Tewkesbury), where I sat up all night
to read *Paul and Virginia*. Sweet were the showers in
early youth that drenched my body, and sweet the drops of
pity that fell upon the books I read! I once hinted to
Wordsworth, as we were sailing in his boat on Grasmere
lake, that I thought he had borrowed the idea of his *Poems
on the Naming of Places* from the local inscriptions of the
same kind in *Paul and Virginia*. He did not own the
obligation, and stated some distinction without a difference
in defence of his claim to originality. Any, the slightest
variation, would be sufficient for this purpose in his mind;
for whatever *he* added or altered would inevitably be worth
all that any one else had done, and contain the marrow of
the sentiment. I was still two days before the time fixed
for my arrival, for I had taken care to set out early enough.
I stopped these two days at Bridgewater; and when I was
tired of sauntering on the banks of its muddy river, returned
to the inn and read *Camilla*. So have I loitered my life
away, reading books, looking at pictures, going to plays,
hearing, thinking, writing on what pleased me best. I have
wanted only one thing to make me happy; but wanting
that, have wanted everything!

"I arrived, and was well received. The country about
Nether Stowey is beautiful, green and hilly, and near the
seashore. I saw it but the other day, after an interval of
twenty years, from a hill near Taunton. How was the map
of my life spread out before me, as the map of the country
lay at my feet! In the afternoon Coleridge took me over to
All-Foxden, a romantic old family mansion of the St. Aubins,
where Wordsworth lived. It was then in the possession of
a friend of the poet's, who gave him the free use of it. Somehow that period (the time just after the French Revolution)
was not a time when *nothing was given for nothing*. The
mind opened, and a softness might be perceived coming over
the heart of individuals beneath 'the scales that fence' our
self-interest. Wordsworth himself was from home, but his
sister kept house, and set before us a frugal repast; and
we had free access to her brother's poems, the *Lyrical*

Ballads, which were still in manuscript, or in the form
of *Sybilline Leaves*. I dipped into a few of these with
great satisfaction, and with the faith of a novice. I
slept that night in an old room with blue hangings, and
covered with the round-faced family portraits of the age of
George I. and II., and from the wooded declivity of the
adjoining park that overlooked my window at the dawn of
day could
> 'Hear the loud stag speak.'

"That morning, as soon as breakfast was over, we strolled
out into the park; and seating ourselves on the trunk of an
old ash-tree that stretched along the ground, Coleridge read
aloud with a sonorous and musical voice the ballad of 'Betty
Foy.' I was not critically or sceptically inclined. I saw
touches of truth and nature, and took the rest for granted.
But in the 'Thorn,' the 'Mad Mother,' and the 'Complaint
of a Poor Indian Woman,' I felt that deeper power and
pathos which have been since acknowledged,

> 'In spite of pride, in erring reason's spite,'

as the characteristics of this author; and the sense of a new
style and a new spirit in poetry came over me. It had to
me something of the effect that arises from the turning up
of the fresh soil, or of the first welcome breath of spring,

> 'While yet the trembling year is unconfirmed.'

Coleridge and myself walked back to Stowey that evening,
and his voice sounded high

> 'Of Providence, foreknowledge, will, and fate,
>   Fix'd fate, free-will, foreknowledge absolute'

as we passed through echoing grove, by fairy stream or water-
fall, gleaming in the summer moonlight! He lamented that
Wordsworth was not prone enough to believe in the traditional
superstitions of the place, and that there was a something cor-
poreal, a *matter-of-factness*, a clinging to the palpable, or

often to the petty, in his poetry, in consequence. His
genius was not a spirit that descended to him through the
air ; it sprung out of the ground like a flower, or unfolded
itself from a green spray, on which the goldfinch sang. He
said, however (if I remember right), that this objection
must be confined to his descriptive pieces ; that his philosophic poetry had a grand and comprehensive spirit in it, so
that his soul seemed to inhabit the universe like a palace,
and to discover truth by intuition rather than by deduction.
The next day Wordsworth arrived from Bristol at Coleridge's cottage. I think I see him now. He answered in
some degree to his friend's description of him, but was more
gaunt and Don Quixote-like. He was quaintly dressed
(according to the *costume* of that unconstrained period) in
a brown fustian jacket and striped pantaloons. There was
something of a roll, a lounge in his gait, not unlike his own
' Peter Bell.' There was a severe, worn pressure of thought
about his temples, a fire in his eye (as if he saw something
in objects more than the outward appearance), an intense,
high, narrow forehead, a Roman nose, cheeks furrowed by
strong purpose and feeling, and a convulsive inclination to
laughter about the mouth, a good deal at variance with the
solemn, stately expression of the rest of his face. Chan-
trey's bust wants the marking traits, but he was teased
into making it regular and heavy ; Haydon's head of him,
introduced into the *Entrance of Christ into Jerusalem*, is
the most like his drooping weight of thought and expression.[1] He sat down and talked very naturally and freely,
with a mixture of clear gushing accents in his voice, a deep
guttural intonation, and a strong tincture of the northern
burr, like the crust on wine. He instantly began to make
havoc of the half of a Cheshire cheese on the table, and said
triumphantly that 'his marriage with experience had not
been so productive as Mr. Southey's in teaching him a
knowledge of the good things of this life.' He had been to
see the *Castle Spectre* by Monk Lewis while at Bristol, and described it very well. He said ' it fitted the taste of the audi-

----

[1] Hazlitt's own head is introduced into the same picture.

ence like a glove.' This *ad captandum* merit was, however,
by no means a recommendation of it, according to the severe
principles of the new school, which reject rather than court
popular effect. Wordsworth, looking out of the low, lat-
ticed window, said, ' How beautifully the sun sets on that
yellow bank !' I thought within myself, ' With what eyes
these poets see nature !' and ever after, when I saw the
sunset stream upon the objects facing it, conceived I had
made a discovery, or thanked Mr. Wordsworth for having
made one for me ! We went over to All-Foxden again the
day following, and Wordsworth read us the story of ' Peter
Bell ' in the open air ; and the comment upon it by his face
and voice was very different from that of some later critics !
Whatever might be thought of the poem, ' his face was as a
book where men might read strange matters,' and he an-
nounced the fate of his hero in prophetic tones. There is a
chaunt in the recitation both of Coleridge and Wordsworth,
which acts as a spell upon the hearer, and disarms the
judgment. Perhaps they have deceived themselves by
making habitual use of this ambiguous accompaniment.
Coleridge's manner is more full, animated, and varied ;
Wordsworth's more equable, sustained, and internal. The
one might be termed more *dramatic*, the other more *lyrical*.
Coleridge has told me that he himself liked to compose in
walking over uneven ground, or breaking through the straggling branches of a copsewood ; whereas Wordsworth
always wrote (if he could) walking up and down a straight
gravel-walk, or in some spot where the continuity of his
verse met with no collateral interruption. Returning that
same evening, I got into a metaphysical argument with
Wordsworth, while Coleridge was explaining the different
notes of the nightingale to his sister, in which we neither of
us succeeded in making ourselves perfectly clear and intelli-
gible. Thus I passed three weeks at Nether Stowey and in
the neighbourhood, generally devoting the afternoons to a
delightful chat in an arbour made of bark by the poet's
friend Tom Poole, sitting under two fine elm-trees, and listening to the bees humming round us, while we quaffed our
flip. It was agreed, among other things, that we should

make a jaunt down the Bristol Channel as far as Linton.
We set off together on foot — Coleridge, John Chester, and
I.   This Chester was a native of Nether Stowey, one of
those who were attracted to Coleridge's discourse as flies are
to honey, or bees in swarming time to the sound of a brass
pan.   He 'followed in the chase like a dog who hunts, not
like one that made up the cry.'   He had on a brown cloth
coat, boots, and corduroy breeches, was low in stature, bow-
legged, had a drag in his walk like a drover, which he
assisted by a hazel switch, and kept up a sort of trot by the
side of Coleridge, like a running footman by a state coach,
that he might not lose a syllable or sound that fell from
Coleridge's lips.   He told me his private opinion, that
Coleridge was a wonderful man.   He scarcely opened his
lips, much less offered an opinion, the whole way ; yet of
the three, had I to choose during that journey, I would be
John Chester.   He afterwards followed Coleridge into Germany, where the Kantean philosophers were puzzled how
to bring him under any of their categories.   When he sat
down at table with his idol, John's felicity was complete ;
Sir Walter Scott's, or Mr. Blackwood's, when they sat down
at the same table with the King, was not more so.   We
passed Dunster on our right, a small town between the
brow of a hill and the sea.   I remember eyeing it wistfully
as it lay below us : contrasted with the woody scene
around, it looked as clear, as pure, as *embrowned* and ideal
as any landscape I have seen since of Caspar Poussin's or
Domenichino's.   We had a long day's march — our feet
kept time to the echoes of Coleridge's tongue — through
Minehead and by the *Blue Anchor*, and on to Linton,
which we did not reach till near midnight, and where we
had some difficulty in making a lodgment.   We, however,
knocked the people of the house up at last, and we were
repaid for our apprehensions and fatigue by some excellent
rashers of fried bacon and eggs.   The view in coming along
had been splendid.   We walked for miles and miles on dark
brown heaths overlooking the Channel, with the Welsh hills
beyond, and at times descended into little sheltered valleys
close by the seaside, with a smuggler's face scowling by us,

and then had to ascend conical hills with a path winding up
through a coppice to a barren top, like a monk's shaven
crown, from one of which I pointed out to Coleridge's notice
the bare masts of a vessel on the very edge of the horizon,
and within the red-orbed disc of the setting sun, like his
own spectre-ship in the *Ancient Mariner*. At Linton the
character of the seacoast becomes more marked and rugged.
There is a place called the *Valley of Rocks* (I suspect this
was only the poetical name for it), bedded among precipices
overhanging the sea, with rocky caverns beneath, into which
the waves dash, and where the seagull for ever wheels its
screaming flight. On the tops of these are huge stones
thrown transverse, as if an earthquake had tossed them
there, and behind these is a fretwork of perpendicular
rocks, something like the *Giant's Causeway*. A thunder-
storm came on while we were at the inn, and Coleridge was
running out bareheaded to enjoy the commotion of the elements in the *Valley of Rocks;* but as if in spite, the clouds
only muttered a few angry sounds, and let fall a few refreshing drops. Coleridge told me that he and Wordsworth
were to have made this place the scene of a prose tale,
which was to have been in the manner of, but far superior
to, the 'Death of Abel,' but they had relinquished the
design. In the morning of the second day we breakfasted
luxuriously, in an old-fashioned parlour, on tea, toast, eggs,
and honey, in the very sight of the beehives from which it
had been taken, and a garden full of thyme and wild
flowers that had produced it. On this occasion Coleridge
spoke of Virgil's *Georgics*, but not well. I do not think he
had much feeling for the classical or elegant. It was in
this room that we found a little worn-out copy of the *Seasons*, lying in a window-seat, on which Coleridge exclaimed,
' *That* is true fame ! ' He said Thomson was a great poet
rather than a good one ; his style was as meretricious as his
thoughts were natural. He spoke of Cowper as the best
modern poet. He said the *Lyrical Ballads* were an experiment about to be tried by him and Wordsworth, to see how
far the public taste would endure poetry written in a more
natural and simple style than had hitherto been attempted ;

totally discarding the artifices of poetical diction, and making use only of such words as had probably been common in the most ordinary language since the days of Henry II. Some comparison was introduced between Shakespeare and Milton. He said ' he hardly knew which to prefer. Shakespeare appeared to him a mere stripling in the art ; he was as tall and as strong, with infinitely more activity than Milton, but he never appeared to have come to man's estate ; or if he had, he would not have been a man, but a monster.' He spoke with contempt of Gray, and with intolerance of Pope. He did not like the versification of the latter. He observed that ' the ears of these couplet-writers might be charged with having short memories that could not retain the harmony of whole passages.' He thought little of Junius as a writer ; he had a dislike of Dr. Johnson ; and a much higher opinion of Burke as an orator and politician than of Fox or Pitt. He, however, thought him very inferior in richness of style and imagery to some of our elder prose-writers, particularly Jeremy Taylor. He liked Richardson, but not Fielding ; nor could I get him to enter into the merits of *Caleb Williams*. In short, he was profound and discriminating with respect to those authors whom he liked, and where he gave his judgment fair play ; capricious, perverse, and prejudiced in his antipathies and distastes. We loitered on the ' ribbed sea-sands ' in such talk as this a whole morning, and I recollect met with a curious seaweed, of which John Chester told us the country name ! A fisherman gave Coleridge an account of a boy that had been drowned the day before, and that they had tried to save at the risk of their own lives. He said ' he did not know how it was that they ventured, but, sir, we have a *nature* towards one another.' This expression, Coleridge remarked to me, was a fine illustration of that theory of disinterestedness which I (in common with Butler) had adopted. I broached to him an argument of mine to prove that *likeness* was not mere association of ideas. I said that the mark in the sand put one in mind of a man's foot, not because it was part of a former impression of a man's foot (for it was quite new), but because it was like the shape of a man's foot. He assented to the justness of this distinction (which I have explained at length elsewhere, for the benefit of the curious), and John Chester listened ; not from any interest in the subject, but because he was astonished that I should be able to suggest anything to Coleridge that he did not already know. We returned on the third morning, and Coleridge remarked the silent cottage-smoke curling up the valleys where, a few evenings before, we had seen the lights gleaming through the dark.

" In a day or two after we arrived at Stowey, we set out, I on my return home, and he for Germany. It was a Sunday morning, and he was to preach that day for Dr. Toulmin of Taunton. I asked him if he had prepared anything for the occasion? He said he had not even thought of the text, but should as soon as we parted. I did not go to hear him — this was a fault — but we met in the evening at Bridgewater. The next day we had a long day's walk to Bristol, and sat down, I recollect, by a well-side on the road to cool ourselves and satisfy our thirst, when Coleridge repeated to me some descriptive lines from his tragedy of *Remorse ;* which I must say became his mouth and that occasion better than they, some years after, did Mr. Elliston's and the Drury Lane boards —

    ' O memory ! shield me from the world's poor strife,
      And give those scenes thine everlasting life.' " [1]

---

[1] First published in the *Examiner*, Jan. 12, 1817. Reprinted with additions in the *Liberal* (1823), again in *Literary Remains* (1836), ii. 359, and again in *Winterslow* (1850). The quotation I have made, though long, is not complete.

CHAPTER IV

HAZLITT's grandson tells us that the obscurest part of his grandfather's youth succeeds the meeting with Coleridge, and the events Hazlitt has himself recorded which followed immediately upon that great occasion. He still continued to live at Wem under his father's roof, and to torment himself and tease his pen, that must have itched for other matter, about that "Natural Disinterestedness of the Human Mind," which he thought he had discovered, and pined to make plainer to the world than he had been able to do to Coleridge on the Shrewsbury Road. This much belaboured and beloved essay did not get printed till 1805, but it lay fermenting in the mind all these years.

This also was the time, 1799–1802, when Hazlitt made that intimate, soul-searching acquaintance with the poetry of Coleridge and Wordsworth which enabled him at any time with equal dexterity to please with exquisite praise or to wound with deadly sarcasm the self-love of its producers. There have been many Wordsworthians during the last hundred years; but never a man among them knew Wordsworth's poetry more intimately, or entered into its true unfettered spirit with greater reality than Hazlitt. No finer compliment can be paid a poet than to let the best of him become a portion of your being. Whenever

Hazlitt was stirred to his depths, we may discern Wordsworth moving on the face of the waters.

In 1799 Crabb Robinson, in that diary of his which is of so much assistance in helping one to trace the history of feeling during the early part of the last century, mentions how he met Hazlitt, then just of age, and reckoned him one of the cleverest men he had ever seen — which in 1799 was perhaps not saying much, but a compliment was intended. Robinson, like Hazlitt, had been brought up among Socinians, and in some respects they were like-minded, but their temperaments were as different as their destinies. Robinson stands eternally in Hazlitt's debt; for it was to Hazlitt he owed his introduction to the *Lyrical Ballads* and the poems generally of Coleridge, Wordsworth, and Lamb. An introduction indeed! What gift could any fairy godmother bestow equal to that of having your face turned early to the light? As time went on the good Robinson, as Carlyle might say, found Hazlitt not a little trying; his style, like Burke's, was forked, and crested as a serpent's; he was not of the stuff poet-worshippers are made of; his "tap" was too bitter, his stride too long, his point of view too independent to suit Robinson, who, living down to our own day, used to suffer agony when his brilliant young friend Walter Bagehot would vehemently express his preference for Hazlitt over Lamb. "You, sir," so Robinson would cry in his anguish, "you prefer the works of that scoundrel, that odious, that malignant writer, to the exquisite essays of that angelic creature!"

Hazlitt, though mainly at Wem, continued to visit his brother John in London. John had many friends, all of a liberal hue — Godwins, Wollstonecrafts, Holcrofts, Rickmans, Burneys, and the like; and through these, or some of them, Hazlitt made the acquaintance of the man — of all the men then living in London the one best worth knowing — Charles Lamb. Him he met for the first time at the Godwins', where a dispute was going on of rather an undergraduate complexion, a "boshy" kind of talk, as to whether it were best to have man as he was or as he is to be. Coleridge said one thing, and Godwin another, and Holcroft both, when Lamb stuttered forth, "Give me man as he is *not* to be." Long friendships are often founded on stray remarks — the one between Johnson and Reynolds, for example — and this saying of Lamb's took Hazlitt by storm and established relations which, though not unbroken, were always renewed, and continued to the bitter end. The exact date of their first meeting is not known; it may have been in the eighteenth century, but probably it was in the nineteenth.

Hazlitt also at this time became intimate with John Stoddart, whose sister Sarah he was to marry later on. John and Sarah were the only children of a retired lieutenant in the navy who lived at Salisbury, and had a small property at Winterslow. John was at this time a student of the Civil Law and a member of Lincoln's Inn, of strong revolution principles, and a hater of William Pitt. He seems to have persuaded Hazlitt to attend with him a famous course of lectures on "Things in General," delivered in Lincoln's Inn Hall by Mackintosh. Three references to these lectures are to be found in some "Remarks on the Systems of Hartley and Helvetius," which Hazlitt printed in 1806 along with his essay "In Defence of the Natural

Disinterestedness of the Human Mind." It must have
been a wonderful course of lectures ; but I cannot
believe the lectures themselves were so well worth
hearing as Hazlitt's account of them is still worth
reading : —

" There was a greater degree of power, or of dashing and
splendid effect (we wish we could add, an equally humane
and liberal spirit), in the ' Lectures on the Law of Nature
and Nations,' formerly delivered by Sir James (then Mr.)
Mackintosh in Lincoln's Inn Hall. He showed greater confidence ; was more at home there. The effect was more
electrical and instantaneous, and this elicited a prouder display of intellectual riches and a more animated and imposing
mode of delivery. He grew wanton with success. Dazzling
others by the brilliancy of his acquirements, dazzled himself
by the admiration they excited, he lost fear as well as prudence ; dared everything, carried everything before him.
The Modern Philosophy, counter-scarp, outworks, citadel,
and all, fell without a blow, by ' the whiff and wind of his
fell *doctrine,*' as if it had been a pack of cards. The volcano of the French Revolution was seen expiring in its own
flames, like a bonfire made of straw ; the principles of
Reform were scattered in all directions, like chaff before the
keen northern blast. He laid about him like one inspired ;
nothing could withstand his envenomed tooth. Like some
savage beast got into the garden of the fabled Hesperides,
he made clear work of it, root and branch, with white,
foaming tusks —

' Laid waste the borders, and o'erthrew the bowers.'

The havoc was amazing, the desolation was complete. As
to our visionary sceptics and Utopian philosophers, they stood
no chance with our lecturer ; he did not ' carve them as a
dish fit for the gods, but hewed them as a carcase fit for
hounds.' Poor Godwin, who had come, in the *bonhomie*
and candour of his nature, to hear what new light had
broken in upon his old friend, was obliged to quit the field,

and slunk away after an exulting taunt thrown out at 'such fanciful chimeras as a golden mountain or a perfect man.' Mr. Mackintosh had something of the air, much of the dexterity and self-possession, of a political and philosophical juggler; and an eager and admiring audience gaped and greedily swallowed the gilded bait of sophistry, prepared for their credulity and wonder. Those of us who attended day after day, and were accustomed to have all our previous notions confounded and struck out of our hands by some metaphysical legerdemain, were at last at some loss to know *whether two and two make four* till we had heard the lecturer's opinion on that head. He might have some mental reservation on the subject, some pointed ridicule to pour upon the common supposition, some learned authority to quote against it. It seemed to be equally his object, or the tendency of his discourses, to unsettle every principle of reason or of common sense, and to leave his audience at the mercy of the *dictum* of a lawyer, the nod of a minister, or the shout of a mob. To effect this purpose, he drew largely on the learning of antiquity, on modern literature, on history, poetry, and the belles-lettres, on the Schoolmen, and on writers of novels, French, English, and Italian. In mixing up the sparkling julep, that by its potent operation was to scour away the dregs and feculence and peccant humours of the body politic, he seemed to stand with his back to the drawers in a metaphysical dispensary, and to take out of them whatever ingredients suited his purpose. In this way he had an antidote for every error, an answer to every folly. The writings of Burke, Hume, Berkeley, Paley, Lord Bacon, Jeremy Taylor, Grotius, Puffendorf, Cicero, Aristotle, Tacitus, Livy, Sully, Machiavelli, Guicciardini, Thuanus, lay open beside him, and he could instantly lay his hand upon the passage, and quote them chapter and verse to the clearing up of all difficulties and the silencing of all oppugners." [1]

The friendship between John Stoddart and Hazlitt was not a lasting one. The former went to Malta as

---

[1] ' Sir James Mackintosh.' — *The Spirit of the Age.*

King's Advocate in 1803, taking his sister with him,
and there the following year Coleridge visited him
and grew painfully interested in Sir Alexander Ball,
as all of us who once thought it a duty to read *The
Friend* know to our cost.

But I have not yet reached 1803. The new century
brings us face to face with a difficulty in Hazlitt's life.
How came it about that he, still in labour with his
Metaphysical Essay, but full to the brim of the new
wine of Coleridge and Wordsworth, and the " old
October " of Congreve and Fielding, suddenly comes
before us as a painter? I have already referred to his
brother's influence, but that had always been at work.
Why had he let so many years slip by? It is not
to be supposed he ever meant to be a preacher — an
author he cannot have dreamt of being — as a means
of livelihood Metaphysics are not to be thought of;
besides, he could not so much as finish one small
essay. A painter he had determined to be in boyhood. Why did he postpone it so long, and why having done so, did he begin it now?

His own account is as follows : —

" My first initiation in the mysteries of the art was at
the Orleans Gallery ; it was there I formed my taste, such
as it is, so that I am irreclaimably of the old school in
painting. I was staggered when I saw the works there
collected, and looked at them with wondering and with
longing eyes. A mist passed away from my sight ; the
scales fell off. A new sense came upon me. I saw the soul
speaking in the face — 'hands that the rod of empire had
swayed ' in mighty ages past — 'a forked mountain or blue
promontory,'

'With trees upon 't
That nod unto the world, and mock our eyes with air.'

Old Time had unlocked his treasures, and Fame stood portress at the door. We had all heard of the names of Titian, Raphael, Guido, Domenichino, the Caracci; but to see them face to face, to be in the same room with their deathless productions, was like breaking some mighty spell — was almost an effect of necromancy. From that time I lived in a world of pictures. Battles, sieges, speeches in Parliament, seemed mere idle noise and fury, 'signifying nothing,' compared with those mighty works and dreaded names that spoke to me in the eternal silence of thought. This was the more remarkable, as it was but a short time before that I was not only totally ignorant of, but insensible to the beauties of art. As an instance, I remember that one afternoon I was reading the *Provoked Husband* with the highest relish, with a green woody landscape of Ruysdael or Hobbima just before me, at which I looked off the book now and then, and wondered what there could be in that sort of work to satisfy or delight the mind — at the same time asking myself, as a speculative question, whether I should ever feel an interest in it like what I took in reading Vanbrugh and Cibber?"[1]

But the Orleans Gallery was in Paris, whither Hazlitt did not go until 1802, after he had made up his mind to be a painter, and had worked hard for a season to fit himself to be one. Northcote, whose acquaintance Hazlitt had made early in the century, may have had something to do with his sudden resolution; and it has been suggested that reading Richardson's *Essays on the Fine Arts* greatly affected his mind. The Rembrandt at Burleigh House had something to do with it. A painter he decided to be; and set to work with so great a fury, that somehow or other he made enough progress, real or apparent, to enable him to obtain a commission from a Manchester man, who wanted to

---

[1] 'On the Pleasure of Painting.' — *Criticisms on Art.*

live surrounded by copies of the old masters, to go to
the Louvre and reproduce Titian.

To the Louvre Hazlitt went in October 1802, and in
Paris he remained four of the happiest months of his
or any man's life. His life in Paris was a hard one;
the weather was bitter cold, his lodgings were poor,
his purse empty, but his power of enjoyment, like the
gaiety of Falstaff or the good-nature of my Uncle
Toby, breaks the bounds of his individuality and over-
flows the world. Both his mind and his brush were
kept hard at work, and feverishly happy.

"I had made some progress in painting when I went to
the Louvre to study, and I never did anything afterwards.
I shall never forget conning over the catalogue which a friend
lent me just before I set out. The pictures, the names of
the painters, seemed to relish in the mouth. There was one
of Titian's 'Mistress at her Toilette.' Even the colours with
which the painter had adorned her hair were not more golden,
more amiable to sight, than those which played round and
tantalised my fancy ere I saw the picture. There were two
portraits by the same hand — 'A Young Nobleman with a
glove'; another, 'A Companion to it.' I read the description over and over with fond expectancy; and filled up the
imaginary outline with whatever I could conceive of grace,
and dignity, and an antique *gusto* — all but equal to the
original. There was 'The Transfiguration' too. With what
awe I saw it in my mind's eye, and was overshadowed with
the spirit of the artist! Not to have been disappointed with
these works afterwards was the highest compliment I can pay
to their transcendent merits. Indeed, it was from seeing other
works of the same great masters that I had formed a vague,
but no disparaging, idea of these. The first day I got there
I was kept for some time in the French Exhibition room, and
thought I should not be able to get a sight of the old masters.
I just caught a peep at them through the door (vile hin-
drance), like looking out of Purgatory into Paradise — from

Poussin's noble, mellow-looking landscapes to where Rubens hung out his gaudy banner, and down the glimmering vista to the rich jewels of Titian and the Italian school. At last, by much importunity, I was admitted, and lost not an instant in making use of my new privilege. It was *un beau jour* to me. I marched delighted through a quarter of a mile of the proudest efforts of the mind of man, a whole creation of genius, a universe of art! I ran the gauntlet of all the schools from the bottom to the top; and in the end got admitted into the inner room, where they had been repairing some of their greatest works. Here 'The Transfiguration,' the 'St. Peter Martyr,' and the 'St. Jerome' of Domenichino stood on the floor, as if they had bent their knees, like camels stooping, to unlade their riches to the spectator. On one side, on an easel, stood 'Hippolito de Medici' (a portrait by Titian), with a boar-spear in his hand, looking through those he saw, till you turned away from the keen glance; and thrown together in heaps were landscapes of the same hand, green pastoral hills and vales, and shepherds piping to their mild mistresses underneath the flowering shade. Reader, 'if thou hast not seen the Louvre, thou art damned!' — for thou hast not seen the choicest remains of the works of art; or thou hast not seen all these together, with their mutually reflected glories. I say nothing of the statues; for I know but little of sculpture, and never liked any till I saw the Elgin marbles. . . . Here, for four months together, I strolled and studied, and daily heard the warning sound, '*Quatre heures passées, il faut fermer, Citoyens*' (ah! why did they ever change their style?), muttered in coarse provincial French; and brought away with me some loose draughts and fragments, which I have been forced to part with, like drops of life-blood, for 'hard money.' How often, thou tenantless mansion of God-like magnificence — how often has my heart since gone a pilgrimage to thee." [1]

Writing in his later life, Hazlitt says that when he was at the Louvre nothing would serve his turn but heads like Titian; but this is not strictly true. No

[1] 'On the Pleasure of Painting.' — *Criticisms on Art.*

man's taste is immaculate; and Hazlitt, surrounded though he was with all the glories of the Louvre of 1802, then rich with the loot of Rome and Dresden, "triumphant spoils" is Hazlitt's own phrase, fell in love with a picture by Lana, "The Death of Clorinda," which he describes in a letter to his father, so graphically suggestive of all its imbecilities, that the conclusion comes like a pistol-shot. "It is in my mind the sweetest picture in the place." One is forced to remember how Hazlitt preferred Warton's *Sonnets* to Shakespeare's. At least a fortnight was devoted to copying the charms of the expiring Clorinda, who points to her wounded breast and awaits baptism at the hands of Tancred, whose helmet serves as font. In 1867 this copy, always dear to Hazlitt, was still " in possession of the family." [1]

Whilst absent from home Hazlitt was a good correspondent, and tells his father how much disappointed he was not to see the First Consul, who was away from Paris. Charles Fox he did see, going the round of the pictures, speaking rapidly but unaffectedly, " All those blues and greens and reds are the Guercinos, you may know them by their colours." " He talked a great deal, and was full of admiration." Fox was the last man to have acted in the spirit of Carlyle's gloomy admonition, " to perambulate your picture gallery in silence."

When Hazlitt left Paris in January in 1803 he carried away with him at least eleven copies he had made in the Louvre, " The Death of Clorinda," Titian's " Man in Black," Titian's " Mistress," " A Holy Family"

---

[1] The original is to be seen in the Turin Gallery.

by Raphael, "The Deluge" by Poussin, various figures from "The Transfiguration," and the sketch of a head from Tintoret being among the number.

For three years after his return from Paris Hazlitt led the life of an itinerant portrait painter. He had a capital pair of legs, loved the road, and wielded the brush with great courage. He was not a timid painter. A man who could paint a recognisable portrait in oils, with an undoubted suggestion of Rembrandt about it, and would do so for five guineas, was not likely to be without work in the north of England. "Kings lay aside their crowns to sit for their portraits, and poets their laurels to sit for their busts. The beggar in the street is proud to have his picture painted, and will almost sit for nothing." Hazlitt began with the poets — the two finest in England, if not in Europe, Coleridge and Wordsworth, whose equine physiognomy Hazlitt greatly admired. Unluckily, neither picture was a success. According to Southey, Hazlitt made Coleridge look like a horse-stealer on his trial, evidently guilty, but clever enough to have a chance of getting off; whilst the Wordsworth, according to another critic, represented a man upon the gallows-tree deeply affected by a fate he felt to be deserved. Failures no doubt, but not insipid failures. Hazlitt also painted the little Hartley Coleridge, reserved for an unkind fate, but who lives for ever "a happy child" in Wordsworth's verse.

Hazlitt is said when in Cumberland to have fallen in love both with Dorothy Wordsworth and with a village beauty, and narrowly to have escaped ducking in a pond by a rival for the hand or favours of the latter. Hazlitt's love affairs are either too shadowy or too silly to bear investigation. The less we can manage to say about them (though the shadows can do us no harm), the better it will be.

From Keswick the painter proceeded to Manchester, where he had friends and acquaintances. Here he painted a half-length portrait of a manufacturer "who died worth a plum"; and as the artist had been living, as an experiment, so he assures us, for a fortnight on coffee, and was very hungry, he rather slurred over the coat, which was a reddish brown, in order that he might feel the manufacturer's five guineas in the pocket. As soon as the guineas were safe, Hazlitt hurried to the market-place and dined on sausages and mashed potatoes, "a noble dish for strong stomachs; and while they were getting ready, and I could hear them hissing on the pan, I read a volume of *Gil Blas*, containing the account of the fair Aurora." Already was Literature beginning to reassert herself.

It was near Manchester that Hazlitt painted the *Head of the Old Woman* about which he has so much to tell us in his essay *On the Pleasures of Painting:* —

"The first head I ever tried to paint was an old woman with the upper part of the face shaded by her bonnet, and I certainly laboured it with great perseverance. It took me numberless sittings to do it. I have it by me still, and sometimes look at it with surprise, to think how much pains were thrown away to little purpose; yet not altogether in vain if it taught me to see good in everything, and to know that there is nothing vulgar in Nature seen with the eye of science or of true art. Refinement creates beauty everywhere; it is the grossness of the spectator that discovers nothing but grossness in the object. Be this as it may, I spared no pains to do my best. If art was long, I thought that life was so too at that moment. I got in the general

effect the first day ; and pleased and surprised enough I was
at my success. The rest was a work of time — of weeks
and months (if need were) of patient toil and careful finishing. I had seen an old head by Rembrandt at Burleigh
House ; and if I could produce a head at all like Rembrandt
in a year, in my lifetime, it would be glory and felicity and
wealth and fame enough for me ! The head I had seen at
Burleigh was an exact and wonderful facsimile of Nature,
and I resolved to make mine (as nearly as I could) an exact
facsimile of Nature. I did not then, nor do I now believe,
with Sir Joshua, that the perfection of art consists in giving
general appearances without individual details, but in giving
general appearances with individual details. Otherwise, I
had done my work the first day. But I saw something
more in Nature than general effect, and I thought it worth
my while to give it in the picture. There was a gorgeous
effect of light and shade ; but there was a delicacy as well as
depth in the chiaroscuro, which I was bound to follow into
all its dim and scarce perceptible variety of tone and shadow.
Then I had to make the transition from a strong light to as
dark a shade, preserving the masses, but gradually softening
off the intermediate parts. It was so in Nature ; the difficulty was to make it so in the copy. I tried, and failed
again and again ; I strove harder, and succeeded as I thought.
The wrinkles in Rembrandt were not hard lines, but broken
and irregular. I saw the same appearance in Nature, and
strained every nerve to give it. If I could hit off this edgy
appearance, and insert the reflected light in the furrows of
old age in half a morning, I did not think I had lost a day.
Beneath the shrivelled yellow parchment look of the skin
there was here and there a streak of the blood colour tinging
the face ; this I made a point of conveying, and did not
cease to compare what I saw with what I did (with jealous
lynx-eyed watchfulness) till I succeeded to the best of my
ability and judgment. How many revisions were there !
How many attempts to catch an expression which I had seen
the day before ! How often did we try to get the old position,
and wait for the return of the same light ! There was a
puckering up of the lips, a cautious introversion of the eye

under the shadow of the bonnet, indicative of the feebleness
and suspicion of old age, which at last we managed, after
many trials and some quarrels, to a tolerable nicety.   The
picture was never finished, and I might have gone on with
it to the present hour.[1] I used to set it on the ground when
my day's work was done, and saw revealed to me with swim-
ming eyes the birth of new hopes and of a new world of
objects.   The painter thus learns to look at Nature with
different eyes.   He before saw her ' as in a glass darkly, but
now face to face.'   He understands the texture and meaning
of the visible universe, and ' sees into the life of things,' not
by the help of mechanical instruments, but of the improved
exercise of his faculties, and an intimate sympathy with
Nature.   The meanest thing is not lost upon him, for he
looks at it with an eye to itself, not merely to his own
vanity or interest, or the opinion of the world.   Even where
there is neither beauty nor use — if that ever were — still
there is truth, and a sufficient source of gratification in the
indulgence of curiosity and activity of mind.   The humblest
painter is a true scholar ; and the best of scholars — the
scholar of Nature.   For myself, and for the real comfort and
satisfaction of the thing, I had rather have been Jan Steen,
or Gerard Dow, than the greatest casuist or philologer that
ever lived." [2]

At Gateacre, a village near Liverpool, he painted
a head of Dr. Shepherd, a friend of his father's, and
the minister of the Unitarian chapel — the father,
so it is believed, of a certain Sally Shepherd who
occasionally whisks her petticoats across the page of
an essay.

In 1804 Hazlitt painted his father's portrait, and
his account of his doing so I will reprint, familiar as it

[1] It is at present covered with a thick slough of oil and varnish
(the perishable vehicle of the English school), like an envelope of
gold-beaters' skin, so as to be hardly visible. -- Note by W. C. H.

[2] ' On the Pleasures of Painting.' — *Criticisms on Art.*

must be to many. He calls the picture one of his first
attempts, but it was hardly that : —

" One of my first attempts was a picture of my father, who
was then in a green old age, with strong-marked features, and
scarred with the smallpox.   I drew it with a broad light
crossing the face, looking down, with spectacles on, reading.
The book was Shaftesbury's *Characteristics*, in a fine old
binding, with Gibelin's etchings.   My father would as lief it
had been any other book ; but for him to read was to be
content, was ' riches fineless.' The sketch promised well ; and
I set to work to finish it, determined to spare no time nor
pains. My father was willing to sit as long as I pleased ; for
there is a natural desire in the mind of man to sit for one's
picture, to be the object of continued attention, to have one's
likeness multiplied ; and besides his satisfaction in the picture,
he had some pride in the artist, though he would rather I
should have written a sermon than painted like Rembrandt or
like Raphael.   Those winter days, with the gleams of sunshine coming through the chapel windows, and cheered by the
notes of the robin redbreast in our garden (that ' ever in the
haunch of winter sings ') — as my afternoon's work drew to a
close — were among the happiest of my life.   When I gave
the effect I intended to any part of the picture for which I
had prepared my colours, when I imitated the roughness of
the skin by a lucky stroke of the pencil, when I hit the clear
pearly tone of a vein, when I gave the ruddy complexion of
health, the blood circulating under the broad shadows of one
side of the face, I thought my fortune made, in my fancying
that I might one day be able to say with Correggio, ' I also
am a painter ! ' It was an idle thought, a boy's conceit ; but
it did not make me less happy at the time.   I used regularly
to set my work in the chair to look at it through the long
evenings ; and many a time did I return to take leave of it
before I could go to bed at night. I remember sending it with
a throbbing heart to the Exhibition, and seeing it hung up
there by the side of one of the Honourable Mr. Skeffington
(now Sir George).   There was nothing in common between
them, but that they were the portraits of two very good-
natured men.

"The picture is left; the table, the chair, the window where I learned to construe Livy, the chapel where my father preached, remain where they were; but he himself is gone to rest, full of years, of faith, of hope, and charity!"[1]

It had been suggested that as Hazlitt began his career as a portrait painter by falling in love with two damsels of different degree in Cumberland, he brought it to an end by actually courting a Miss Railton, the daughter of an old friend and patron in Liverpool. John Hazlitt made a beautiful miniature portrait of this lady, but the affair came to nothing, and the vision of Miss Railton joins the other shadows, and even has the honour in the essay "On Reading Old Books" to be associated with Miss Walton, the heroine in the *Man of Feeling*. "I have a sneaking kindness for Mackenzie's *Julia de Roubigné*; for the deserted mansion and struggling gilliflowers on the mouldering garden wall; and still more, for his *Man of Feeling*, not that it is better, nor so good, but at the time I read it I sometimes thought of the heroine Miss Walton and of Miss Railton together, 'and that ligament, fine as it was, was never broken.'"

Hazlitt, it must never be forgotten, was a sentimentalist of the first water.

His last portrait known to fame is the one of Charles Lamb which, after the vicissitudes of the auction-room, is now safely lodged in the National Portrait Gallery. It is a capital specimen of Hazlitt's style.

In 1805 Hazlitt abandoned painting as a profes-

[1] 'On the Pleasures of Painting.' — *Criticisms on Art.*

sion. He never scaled as a painter the steep stair-
case that leads to the mastery of any art. In an
essay contributed near the end of his life to a magazine, and called *English Students at Rome*,[1] he had
(I think) himself and his own failure in mind when
he wrote : —

"The brooding over excellence with a feverish importunity, and stimulating ourselves to great things by an abstract
love of fame, can do little good, and may do much harm. It
is, no doubt, a very delightful and enviable state of mind to
be in, but neither a very arduous nor a very profitable one.
Nothing remarkable was ever done, except by following up
the impulse of our own minds, by grappling with difficulties
and improving our advantages, not by dreaming over our
own premature triumphs, or doting on the achievements of
others."

[1] Reprinted in *Criticisms on Art*.

CHAPTER V

HAZLITT'S first book was that *Essay in Defence of the Natural Disinterestedness of the Human Mind,* or, as he sometimes called it, *On the Principles of Human Action,* which had for too many years weighed so heavily on his own mind. To this disquisition were added *Some Remarks on the Systems of Hartley and Helvetius.* The publisher was good-natured Mr. Johnson, Cowper's friend, who had already printed the *Select Discourses* of the elder Hazlitt, and enabled that excellent man to send a copy to Mrs. Tracy in Liverpool. The date of the first edition of Hazlitt's metaphysical essay was 1805. After a lapse of more than thirty years, namely, in 1836, when its author had disappeared " from the banks and shoal of time," Mr. John Miller of Oxford Street, a man, so Mr. Ireland notes, " of thought and intelligence, and a member of the Debating Society described in *Daniel Deronda,*" brought out a second edition of the *Essay* and *Remarks,* and added an unpublished paper on *Abstract Ideas,* the whole making a tiny book of 176 pages, and dedicated in the name of the departed author to " Edward Lytton Bulwer, M.P., one of the brightest ornaments of his country."

Neither in 1805, nor in 1836, nor at any time since, did Hazlitt's metaphysical discovery attract attention. Nobody minded it. A copy was sent out to Mackintosh,

who, says an enthusiastic admirer of Hazlitt, was able
"even amid the enervating heat of Hindostan" to pro-
nounce it "a work of great ability." Its one eloquent
passage was said by Southey, who hated Hazlitt, not
without reason, to be something between the manner
of Milton and Jeremy Taylor. But the metaphysicians
cannot be brought to take any interest in the essay,
and Mr. Leslie Stephen dismisses it with frigid
indifference.[1]

It is, however, useful to remember that Hazlitt
commenced author as a metaphysician and that amid
all his sensuous enjoyment of what are called realities,
of Mrs. Siddons rubbing her hands in the night scene
of Macbeth, of the sound of Mrs. Jordan's voice,
perhaps as Miss Prue in *Love for Love*, "whose laugh
was to drink nectar," of the azure skies and golden
sunsets of Claude, of the smooth ivory foreheads of
Vandyke, of an old play, or a new Waverley novel,
Hazlitt ever entertained an equally passionate attachment to abstract ideas and general propositions.

It would be unpardonable for a biographer of Hazlitt
not to state what was his metaphysical discovery; and
I will do so, not in the hard dry style of the original
communication, but by a few extracts from the letter to
Gifford (1819), at the end of which the writer insisted
upon repeating and restating at great length his discovery : —

> "I have been called a writer of third-rate books. For
> myself there is no work of mine which I should rate so high,
> except one which I daresay you have never heard of — an
> *Essay on the Principles of Human Action*."

---

[1] See *Hours in a Library*. — 'William Hazlitt.'

"The object of that essay is to remove a stumblingblock in the metaphysical doctrine of the innate and necessary selfishness of the human mind."

" This doctrine, which has been sedulously and confidently maintained by Hobbes, etc., and is a corner-stone of what is called Modern Philosophy, has done a great deal of mischief, and I believe I have found out a view of the subject which gets rid of it unanswerably and for ever."

" The word SELF denotes *three* different selves— my *Past* self, my *Present* self, and my *Future* self, and my personal identity is founded only on my personal consciousness, *which does not extend beyond the present moment.*"

" I have a peculiar, exclusive self-interest or sympathy with my PRESENT SELF by means of *Sensation*, and with my PAST SELF by means of *Memory;* but I have no peculiar exclusive or independent faculty, like *Sensation* or *Memory*, giving me the same instinctive interest in my FUTURE SELF."

" The only faculty by which I can anticipate what is to befall myself in the FUTURE is the *Imagination*, which is not a limited narrow faculty, but *common, discursive,* and *social.*"

" It may be said that I do feel an interest in my own future welfare which I do not and cannot feel in that of others. *This I grant;* but that does not prove a metaphysical ante-cedent, self-interest, precluding the possibility of all interest in others, but a practical self-interest arising out of habit and circumstance."

" My *identity* with myself must be confined to the con-nection between my *past* and *present* being; for how can this pretended unity of consciousness, which makes me so little acquainted with the future that I cannot tell for a moment how long it will be continued, or whether it will be entirely interrupted by death, or renewed in me after death, or multi-plied in I don't know how many different persons — how, I ask, can a principle of this sort transfuse my present into my future being ? "

This seems to me, who am not a metaphysician, sensible enough, but lamentably unimportant.   Man *need not* be selfish with regard to the future, but habit and circumstance will probably, though not inevitably, make him so; and as most men think it right to provide for the morrow, the imagination is likely to prove as active a source of selfishness as either sensation or memory. But selfishness is not innate — that seems to be the discovery.

The passage Southey admired ran as follows : —

"There are moments in the life of a solitary thinker which are to him what the evening of some great victory is to the conqueror and hero — though milder triumphs are long remembered with truer and deeper delight. And though the shouts of multitudes do not hail his success, though gay trophies, though the sounds of music, the glittering of armour, and the neighing of steeds do not mingle with his joy, yet shall he not want monuments and witnesses of his glory ; the deep forest, the willowy brook, the gathering clouds of winter, or the silent gloom of his own chamber, 'faithful remembrances of his high endeavour and his glad success,' that, as time passes by him with unreturning wing, still awaken the consciousness of a spirit patient and indefatigable in the search of truth, and a hope of surviving in the thoughts and minds of other men."

The publication of this little book in 1805 was a great relief to Hazlitt, if no great benefit to the world. He says about it: " I felt a certain weight and tightness about my heart taken off, and cheerful and confident thought springing up in the place of anxious fears and sad forebodings."

His next publication (1806) was a political pamphlet, writ in the new style which was now to be his. It was called *Free Thoughts on Public Affairs, or Advice to a Patriot, in a Letter Addressed to a Member of the Old Opposition.* This pamphlet was admittedly inspired

by a famous article of Coleridge's which had appeared
in the *Morning Post* six years before—on the 19th of
March 1800—and what Hazlitt has to say in his
pamphlet about the character of Pitt was almost word
for word the same with what Coleridge had already
said in the *Morning Post.*

The pamphlet had no sale, and but one copy is
believed to exist; but as Hazlitt thought fit more than
ten years afterwards to insert "The Character of
Pitt" in the *Round Table* (1817), he thereby enabled
Gifford, who was probably already on the lookout for
a reputed Jacobin, to spit his venom in the *Quarterly
Review* after this fashion: "We are far from intending
to write a single word in answer to this loathsome
trash [the Character of Pitt], but we confess that these
passages chiefly excited us to take the trouble of
noticing the work (the *Round Table*); but if the creature in his endeavour to crawl into the light must
take his way over the tombs of illustrious men, dis-
figuring the records of their greatness with the slime
and filth which marks his track, it is right to point
out to him that he may be flung back to the situation
in which Nature designed that he should grovel."[1]

What a pleasant prospect lay before Hazlitt! It
would have been better for his happiness had he finished his course at Hackney and led the life of his old
friend the Rev. Joseph Fawcett.

Some readers may be curious to have a specimen of
"the slime and filth" which Hazlitt borrowed from
Coleridge's article of 1800, printed in his pamphlet of
1806, and reprinted in the *Round Table* in 1817:—

---

[1] *Quarterly Review*, vol. xvii. p. 159.

"Without insight into human nature, without sympathy with the passions of men, or apprehension of their real designs, he seemed perfectly insensible to the consequences of things, and would believe nothing till it actually happened. The fog and haze in which he saw everything communicated itself to others; and the total indistinctness and uncertainty of his own ideas tended to confound the perceptions of his hearers more effectually than the most ingenious misrepresentation could have done. Indeed, in defending his conduct, he never seemed to consider himself as at all responsible for the success of his measures, or to suppose that future events were in our own power; but that, as the best laid schemes might fail, and there was no providing against all possible contingencies, this was a sufficient excuse for our plunging at once into any dangerous or absurd enterprise without the least regard to consequences. . . . Nothing could ever drive him out of his dull forms and naked generalities, which, as they are susceptible neither of degree nor variation, are therefore equally applicable to every emergency that can happen; and in the most critical aspect of affairs he saw nothing but the same flimsy web of remote possibilities and metaphysical uncertainty. In his mind the wholesome pulp of practical wisdom and salutary advice was immediately converted into the dry chaff and husks of a miserable logic. From his manner of reasoning, he seemed not to have believed that the truth of his statements depended on the reality of the facts, but that the facts themselves depended on the order in which he arranged them in words. You would not suppose him to be agitating a serious question, which had real grounds to go upon, but to be declaiming upon an imaginary thesis, proposed as an exercise in the schools. He never set himself to examine the force of the objections that were brought against him, or attempted to defend his measures upon clear, solid grounds of his own; but constantly contented himself with first gravely stating the logical form, or dilemma to which the question reduced itself; and then, after having declared his opinion, proceeded to amuse his hearers by a series of rhetorical commonplaces, connected together in grave, sonorous, and elaborately con-

structed periods, without ever showing their real application
to the subject in dispute.   Thus, if any member of the opposition disapproved of any measure, and enforced his objections by pointing out the many evils with which it was
fraught, or the difficulties attending its execution, his only
answer was ' that it was true there might be inconveniences
attending the measure proposed, but we were to remember
that every expedient that could be devised might be said to
be nothing more than a choice of difficulties, and that all
that human prudence could do was to consider on which side
the advantages lay ; that, for his part, he conceived that
the present measure was attended with more advantages and
fewer disadvantages than any other that could be adopted ;
that if we were diverted from our object by every appearance of difficulty, the wheels of government would be clogged
by endless delays and imaginary grievances ; that most of
the objections made to the measure appeared to him to be
trivial, others of them unfounded and improbable ; or that,
if a scheme, free from all these objections, could be proposed,
it might, after all, prove inefficient ; while, in the meantime,
a material object remained unprovided for, or the opportunity
of action was lost.' . . .   He has not left behind him a single
memorable saying — not one profound maxim, one solid observation, one forcible description, one beautiful thought, one
humorous picture, one affecting sentiment.   He has made no
addition whatever to the stock of human knowledge.   He
did not possess any one of those faculties which contribute
to the instruction and delight of mankind — depth of understanding, imagination, sensibility, wit, vivacity, clear and
solid judgment."

If this be not true of Pitt, it is, at any rate, true of
other practitioners in the same way of business.

The year 1807 was a busy year in Hazlitt's life.
He expended much time upon, and took great pains
with, an abridgment of Abraham Tucker's *Light of
Nature Pursued*.   Tucker's book is a discursive but
original work in seven large volumes, which have been

more praised than read, and more often pilfered from than quoted. These seven volumes Hazlitt, by masterly compression, reduced to one. Johnson was again its publisher; and Mackintosh, when compiling his dissertation for the *Encyclopœdia Britannica* " On the Progress of Ethical Philosophy," took occasion to praise Hazlitt's preface. In this preface Tucker is described in terms which have always reminded me of Mr. Bagehot : —

" To the ingenuity and closeness of the metaphysician he unites the practical knowledge of the man of the world and the utmost sprightliness and even levity of imagination. He is the only philosopher who appears to have had his senses always *about him*, or to have possessed the enviable faculty of attending at the same time to what was passing in his own mind and what was going on without him. He applied everything to the purposes of philosophy ; he could not see anything, the most familiar objects or the commonest events, without connecting them with the illustration of some difficult problem ; the tricks of a young kitten, or a little child at play, were sure to suggest to him some useful observation or nice distinction."

This passage not only reminds me of Mr. Bagehot, but of a good many passages in Mr. Bagehot's books.

Hazlitt was also engaged this same year in making a selection from great Parliamentary speakers, called *The Eloquence of the British Senate*, to which he added biographical and critical notes. This is a better known book than the abridgment of Tucker; and the sketches it contains of the characters of Chatham, Burke, and Fox are full of insight, vivacity, and fervour. Hazlitt afterwards reprinted these characters in his *Political Essays* (1819).

How quickly Hazlitt found his style after he had purged his bosom of the perilous stuff of metaphysics is well illustrated by the third book he published, anonymously, like the others, during 1807. I mean his *Reply to the Essay on Population by the Rev. T. R. Malthus in a Series of Letters.*

This book is composed in a flowery, almost voluptuous vein, and lacks the control usually characteristic of Hazlitt's style, outspoken and personal though that style may be; but the reader certainly notices in this *Reply to Malthus* the opening of the floodgates of Hazlitt's rhetoric:—

"I never fell in love but once, then it was with a girl who always wore her handkerchief pinned tight round her neck, with a fair face, gentle eyes, a soft smile, and cool auburn locks. It was not a raging heat, a fever in the veins; but it was like a vision, a dream like thoughts of childhood, an everlasting hope, a distant joy, a heaven, a world that might be. The dream is still left, and sometimes comes confusedly over me, in solitude and silence, and mingles with the softness of the sky, and veils my eye from mortal grossness."

An answer to Malthus indeed: akin to Carlyle's more manly strain, "Pretty Sally in my Alley proves too much for stout John in yours."

The book concludes in a nobler spirit, with a passage which pleases, as does Newman's eloquence, by its mingled force and feeling, pith and pity:—

"I have thus attempted to answer the different points of Mr. Malthus's argument, and give a truer account of the various principles that actuate human nature. There is but one advantage that I can conceive of as resulting from the admission of his mechanical theory on the subject, which is that it would be the most effectual recipe for indifference that has yet been found out. No one need give himself any farther trouble about the progress of vice or the extension of misery. The office of moral censor, that troublesome, uneasy office which every one is so ready to set up in his own breast, which I verily believe is the occasion of more unhappiness than any one cause else, would be at an end. The professor's chair of morality would become vacant, and no one would have more cause than I to rejoice at the breaking up for the holidays; for I have plagued myself a good deal about the distinctions of right and wrong. The pilot might let go the helm and leave the vessel to drift carelessly before the stream. When we are once convinced that the degree of virtue and happiness can no more be influenced by human wisdom than the ebbing and flowing of the tide, it must be idle to give ourselves any more concern about them. The wise man might then enjoy an Epicurean languor and repose without being conscious of the neglect of duty. Mr. Malthus's system is one, 'in which the wicked cease from troubling, and in which the weary are at rest.' To persons of an irritable and nervous disposition, who are fond of kicking against the pricks, who have tasted of the bitterness of the knowledge of good and evil, and to whom whatever is amiss in others sticks not merely like a burr, but like a pitch plaister, the advantage of such a system is incalculable.

"Happy are they who live in the dream of their own existence and see all things in the light of their own minds; who walk by faith and hope, not by knowledge; to whom the guiding-star of their youth still shines from afar, and into whom the spirit of the world has not entered! They have not been 'hurt by the archers,' nor has the iron entered their souls. They live in the midst of arrows and of death, unconscious of harm. The evil thing comes not nigh them. The shafts of ridicule pass unheeded by, and malice loses its sting. Their keen perceptions do not catch at hidden mischiefs, nor cling to every folly. The example of vice does not rankle in their breasts, like the poisoned shirt of Nessus. Evil impressions fall off from them, like drops of water. The yoke of life is to them light and supportable. The world has

no hold on them.   They are in it, not of it ; and a dream and
a glory is ever about them."

With Hazlitt's argument against Malthus the reader
will not wish me to concern myself ; but my duty com-
pels me to say that one of the points made against
Malthus he conceived to be original, and somewhat
jealously guarded against De Quincey, who had picked
it up by the way.   Malthus, in Hazlitt's words,
"made a monster of the principle of population," and
in the words of Coleridge, "wrote a quarto volume
to prove that man could not live without eating," a
proposition by no means so terrible in itself but that,
in order to drive his monster home to men's bosoms,
it was necessary for Malthus to promulgate the proposition that whilst the species who live by eating
increase in a geometrical ratio, the means of their
subsistence increase only in an arithmetical ratio.
Hence the gloom of the situation.   But, said Hazlitt,
this is only true when the whole earth is under
culivation.   "A grain of corn has the same or greater
power of propagating its species than a man has till
there is no longer any room for it to grow or spread
further."   Longmans published the book.

None of these efforts can have brought much grist
to the mill ; but as Hazlitt continued to divide his time
between his father's house at Wem and his brother's
studio in London, his expenses cannot have been great,
for he was never an extravagant man.

His friendship with Lamb at this time was at its
height, and he seldom missed a Wednesday evening
in Mitre Court, when Lamb's talk was like "snap-
dragon" and his own "like a game of ninepins."

In Mr. W. C. Hazlitt's pleasant little book *Lamb and Hazlitt* (1900) he supplies the history of an elaborate hoax or "mystification" of the kind in which Elia ever delighted, practised upon Hazlitt about this time, into the humour of which the latter fully entered, and played up to with the utmost spirit. The jest turned upon a report circulated by Lamb and Joseph Hume of the Victualling Office, Somerset House, "that W. H., a portrait painter in Southampton Buildings, Holborn, put an end to his existence by cutting his throat in a shocking manner," and gruesome details follow. Thereupon Hazlitt prepared and presented a lengthy Petition and Remonstrance protesting against the report, and seeking to establish the fact of his continued existence by setting out in twelve paragraphs his manner of life, and concluding thus:—

"With all the sincerity of a man doubtful between life and death, the petitioner declares that he looks upon the said Charles Lamb as the ringleader in this unjust conspiracy against him, and as the sole cause and author of the jeopardy he is in; but that as losers have leave to speak, he must say that, if it were not for a poem he wrote on Tobacco about two years ago, a farce called Mr. H —— he brought out last winter with more wit than discretion in it, some prologues and epilogues he has since written with good success, and some lively notes he is at present writing on dead authors, he sees no reason why he should not be considered as much a dead man as himself, and the undertaker spoken to accordingly.
"A true copy.
                                        "W. HAZLITT.
"Dated Sunday, the 10th of Jany.
        "1808."

Lamb and Hume affected to treat this petition as either a forgery or a ghostly communication, and

about it Lamb descants in a style that is now the
delight of two continents.   After first remarking that
the reason most commonly assigned for the reappearance of disembodied spirits is the revealing of hoarded
treasure, he proceeds: —

"It is highly improbable that he should have accumulated
any such vast treasures, for the revealing of which a miracle
was needed, without some suspicion of the fact among his
friends during his lifetime.   I for my part always looked upon
our dear friend as a man rich rather in the gifts of his mind
than in earthly treasures.   He had few rents or comings in
that I was ever aware of, small (if any) landed property; and
by all that I could witness, he subsisted more upon the well-
timed contributions of a few chosen friends who knew his
worth than upon any estate which could properly be called
his own.   I myself have contributed my part.   God knows,
I speak not this in reproach.   I have never taken, nor indeed
did the deceased offer, any *written acknowledgments* of the
various sums which he has had of me, by which I could make
the fact manifest to the legal eye of an executor or adminis-
trator.   He was not a man to affect these niceties in his
transactions with his friends.   He would often say money
was nothing between intimate acquaintances; that golden
streams had no ebb; that God loved a cheerful giver; that
a paid loan makes angels groan, with many such like sayings.
He had always free and generous notions about money.   His
nearest friends know this best.   Induced by these considera-
tions, I give up that commonly received notion of Revealable
Treasures in our friend's case.   Neither am I too forward to
adopt that vulgar superstition of some hidden murder to be
brought to light, which yet I do not universally reject; for
when I resolve that the defunct was naturally of a discour-
sible and communicative temper (though of a gloomy and close
aspect, as born under Saturn), a great repeater of conversations,
which he generally carried away verbatim, and would repeat
with syllabic exactness in the next company where he was
received (by which means, I that have stayed at home, have

often reaped the profit of his travels without stirring from my
elbow chair), I cannot think that if he had been present at
so remarkable a circumstance as a murder he would so soon
have forgotten it as to make no mention of it at the next
place where he dined or supped, or that he could have re-
strained himself from giving the particulars of a matter of
fact like that in his lifetime. I am sure I have often heard
him dilate upon occurrences of a much less interesting sort
than that in question. I am most inclined to support that
opinion which favours the establishing of some speculative
point in religion : a frequent cause, says Wierus, for spirits
returning to the earth to confute Atheists, etc., when I consider the education which our friend received from a venerable
parent, his religious destination, his nurture at a seminary
appropriated to young ministers. But whatever the cause of
this reappearance may prove to be, we may now with truth
assert that our deceased friend had attained to one object of
his pursuits, one hour's separate existence gives a dead man
clearer notions of metaphysics than all the treatises which in
this state of carnal entanglement the least-immersed spirit can
outspin."

The whole story should be read in the little book
already mentioned.

At an earlier date than this mystification, viz. on the
10th of December 1806, Hazlitt had sat with Lamb in
the front row of the pit in Drury Lane when another
Mr. H—— was undeniably damned — that strange-
fortuned farce which lives for ever in the hour of its
shame. Not to be outdone in kindnesses, Lamb in
his turn, namely, on Sunday the 1st of May 1808,
accompanied Hazlitt to St. Andrew's Church, Holborn,
and stood by and saw his friend married to Miss Sarah
Stoddart.

Between Mary Lamb and Sarah Stoddart there had
long been friendship ; and it was possibly due to the

offices of the most incomparable of old maids that the
marriage of Hazlitt was brought about. Miss Stoddart
was not romantic, but determined to be married,
though with a settlement upon herself and her issue
of her cottages at Winterslow, which produced the
annual sum of £120. She had many affairs of the
heart, all of which she discussed in a business-like
spirit with Miss Lamb, who was greatly amused with
her tales, so unlike those of Shakespeare's women.
Miss Stoddart's letters to her confidante are not forth-
coming; but from Miss Lamb's letters to her, we can
still dimly discern the embarrassed phantoms of a
Mr. Turner, a Mr. White, a Mr. Dowling, and a certain
" William " of partridge-shooting proclivities, all on,
and then, for one reason or another, all off. But Miss
Stoddart's mind to be married with a settlement
remains unchanged.

Mary Lamb, in a letter in which she delicately
inquires what her friend means to do with Mr. Turner,
introduces the name of William Hazlitt. She writes:
" William Hazlitt, the brother of him you know, is in
town. I believe you have heard us say we like him.
He came in good time, for the loss of Manning made
Charles very dull, and he likes Hazlitt better than
anybody except Manning."

Hazlitt and Miss Stoddart were probably known to
one another before the date of this letter; for, as
already mentioned, in 1799, Hazlitt and John Stoddart
were friendly.

How the matter was actually arranged is not known,
though we hear of John Hazlitt's being " mightily
pleased "; but not so John Stoddart, on whom Hazlitt
now looked sourly, for he had married a clergyman's

daughter and abandoned the abstract principles of the
French Revolution, spoke well of legitimate monarchs,
and would no longer drink confusion to the Holy
Alliance. Miss Lamb was full of sympathy, though
she had her doubts, as may be perceived from the
following letter, or end of a letter addressed to Miss
Stoddart : —

"Farewell ! Determine as wisely as you can in regard to
Hazlitt ; and if your determination is to have him, Heaven
send you many happy years together. If I am not mistaken, I have concluded letters on the Corydon courtship
with this same wish. I hope it is not ominous of change ;
for if I were sure you would not be quite starved to death,
nor beaten to a mummy, I should like to see Hazlitt and
you come together, if (as Charles observes) it were only for
the joke sake."

Of Hazlitt's præ-nuptial letters to Miss Stoddart but
one survives. I give part of it : —

"Tuesday night.

"My dear Love, — Above a week has passed, and I
have received no letter — not one of those letters 'in which
I live, or have no life at all.' What is become of you?
Are you married, hearing that I was dead (for so it has been
reported)? Or are you gone into a nunnery? Or are you
fallen in love with some of the amorous heroes of Boccaccio?
Which of them is it? Is it with Cymon, who was transformed from a clown into a lover, and learned to spell by the
force of beauty? Or with Lorenzo, the lover of Isabella,
whom her three brethren hated (as your brother does me),
who was a merchant's clerk? Or with Federigo Alberigi,
an honest gentleman, who ran through his fortune, and won
his mistress by cooking a fair falcon for her dinner, though
it was the only means he had left of getting a dinner for
himself? This last is the man ; and I am the more per-

suaded of it, because I think I won your good liking myself
by giving you an entertainment — of sausages, when I had
no money to buy them with.   Nay now, never deny it!
Did not I ask your consent that very night after, and did
you not give it?   Well, I should be confoundedly jealous of
those fine gallants if I did not know that a living dog is
better than a dead lion; though, now I think of it, Boccaccio
does not in general make much of his lovers — it is his women
who are so delicious.   I almost wish I had lived in those
times, and had been a little *more amiable*.   Now if a
woman had written the book, it would not have had this
effect upon me ; the men would have been heroes and angels,
and the women nothing at all.   Isn't there some truth in
that?   Talking of departed loves, I met my old flame the
other day in the street.   I did dream of her *one* night since,
and only one ; every other night I have had the same dream
I have had for these two months past.   Now, if you are at
all reasonable, this will satisfy you. . . .   For, indeed, I
never love you so well as when I think of sitting down with
you to dinner on a boiled scrag-end of mutton and hot potatoes.   You please my fancy more then than when I think
of you in — no, you would never forgive me if I were to
finish the sentence.   Now I think of it, what do you mean
to be dressed in when we are married?   But it does not
much matter!   I wish you would let your hair grow ; though
perhaps nothing will be better than ' the same air and look
with which first my heart was took.'   But now to business.
I mean soon to call upon your brother *in form*, namely, as
soon as I get quite well, which I hope to do in about another
fortnight ; and then I hope you will come up by the coach
as fast as the horses can carry you, for I long mightily to be
in your ladyship's presence — to vindicate my character.   I
think you had better sell the small house — I mean that at
4.10 — and I will borrow £100.   So that we shall set off
merrily in spite of all the prudence of Edinburgh. — Good-
bye, little dear !   W. H.

     " Miss STODDART,
     " Winterslow, Salisbury, Wilts."

The only guests known to be at Hazlitt's wedding were John Stoddart, commonly called Dr. Stoddart, and his wife, and Charles and Mary Lamb. Charles, as his wont was on solemn occasions, laughed so loudly that he was like to be turned out several times during the ceremony.

Mrs. Hazlitt carried her black-browed lord off to one of her Winterslow cottages. Winterslow is a small village some seven miles from Salisbury on the Andover Road. Stonehenge is nine miles off. Hazlitt loved Salisbury Plain, whose undulating slopes, showing "the earth in its primeval simplicity, bare with naked breasts, varied only by the shadows of the clouds that pass across it," loom large and fade mistily away into the horizon of many of his word pictures.

A New and Improved Grammar of the English Tongue, for the Use of Schools, containing though it is said to do sentiments respecting the substantive and adjective, and new and ingenious remarks on the verb, seems hardly the occupation for a sentimentalist during the first months of married life; but Hazlitt was as angry with the blindness and obstinacy of Lindley Murray as ever he was with the atrocities of Malthus, or of those philosophers who would have us believe that we could be innately selfish with regard to the future. Grammar has its fascinations; and even such men as John Milton and John Wesley, no less than William Cobbett and William Hazlitt, succumbed to its charms.

Hazlitt's Grammar did not find a publisher till 1810, and never found its way into schools at all, where Lindley Murray, in spite of Horne Tooke and Hazlitt, continued to teach that a noun is the name of a thing.

"Is Quackery a thing, *i.e.* a substance?" cries Hazlitt in his wrath.

Painting as a recreation was not wholly abandoned during these years; for in 1809 Hazlitt was working "like Satan" at a picture of "Jacob's Ladder," a subject which had always attracted him.   In a long and pleasant letter to his wife, printed in *Lamb and Hazlitt* (1900), he describes himself as "sometimes glazing and sometimes scumbling, as it happens, now on the wrong side of the canvas and now on the right, but still persuading myself that I have at last found out the true secret of Titian's golden hue and the oleaginous touches of Claude Lorraine.   I have got in a pretty good background, and a *conception* of the ladder which I learned from the upping stone on the down, only making the stone into gold, and a few other improvements.   I have no doubt there was such another on the field of Luz, and that an upping stone is the genuine Jacob's ladder.   But where are the angels to come from?   That's another question, which I am not yet able to solve.   My dear Sarah, I am too tired and too dull to be witty, and therefore I will not attempt it."

In October 1809 the Lambs paid the Hazlitts a visit at Winterslow that long lived in all their memories. "I used to walk out at this time with Mr. and Miss Lamb of an evening, and look at the Claude Lorraine skies over our heads melting from azure into purple and gold, and to gather mushrooms that sprang up at our feet, to throw into our hashed mutton at supper." Of Lamb in the country he makes the quotation that he was "like the most capricious poet Ovid among the Goths."   Hazlitt took his delightful guests to Oxford, where he expanded in the Bodleian, and to Blenheim, where he was a *cicerone* to the pictures; but, as Crabb Robinson told Lamb on the latter's return to London, forgot to show them the Titian Gallery, if indeed it would have been shown to Mrs. Hazlitt and Miss Lamb — such was the delicacy of the noble proprietor. This visit inspired one of the first of the essays of Elia, "Oxford in the Vacation."

Thomas Holcroft, the author of that excellent piece *The Road to Ruin*, had died in 1809, leaving behind him Memoirs, the editing and completing of which was intrusted to Hazlitt, who by the end of 1810 had three volumes (small ones) ready for the press. A fourth is said still to remain in manuscript. It was difficult to find or agree upon a publisher, and Mary Lamb writes to Mrs. Hazlitt in November 1810: "Mrs. Holcroft still goes about from Nicholson to Tuthill, from Tuthill to Godwin, and from Godwin to Tuthill, and from Tuthill to Nicholson, to consult on the publication or no-publication of that good man her husband. It is called *The Life Everlasting*. How does that same life get on in your hands?" The three volumes were published in 1816, and are good reading — particularly in the early parts.

Such leisure as Hazlitt had at this time he devoted to a careful study of Hobbes, Berkeley, Locke, Butler, and other philosophers, English and French, for he had begun to meditate a history of English philosophy.

On the 26th of September 1811 the future Registrar in Bankruptcy was born, the second child of the marriage, the firstborn having died at Winterslow in July 1809.

Nobody's birth, not even the *Child Angel's* in the

essay of Elia, was ever made the subject of pleasanter congratulations than those which reached Winterslow from the Temple.   Miss Lamb wrote to the mother, and her brother to the father : —

"2 Oct. 1811, Temple.

"My dear Sarah, — I have been a long time anxiously expecting the happy news that I have just received.   I address you because, as the letter has been lying some days at the India House, I hope you are able to sit up and read my congratulations on the little live boy you have been so many years wishing for.   As we old women say, ' May he live to be a great comfort to you.'   I never knew an event of the kind that gave me so much pleasure as the little, long-looked-for, come-at-last's arrival ; and I rejoice to hear his honour has begun to suck.   The word was not distinctly written, and I was a long time making out the wholesome fact.   I hope to hear from you soon, for I am anxious to know if your nursing labours are attended with any difficulties.   I wish you a happy *getting-up* and a merry christening.

"Charles sends his love, perhaps though he will write a scrap to Hazlitt at the end.   He is now looking over me ; he is always in my way, for he has had a month's holiday at home ; but I am happy to say they end on Monday, when mine begin, for I am going to pass a week at Richmond with Mrs. Burney.   She had been dying ; but she went to the Isle of Wight and recovered once more.   When there I intend to read novels and play at piquet all day long. — Yours truly,
"M. Lamb."

"Dear Hazlitt, — I cannot help accompanying my sister's congratulations to Sarah with some of my own to you on this happy occasion of a man child being born.

"Delighted fancy already sees him some future rich alderman or opulent merchant, painting perhaps a little in his leisure hours for amusement, like the late H. Bunbury, Esq.

"Pray, are the Winterslow estates entailed ?   I am afraid

lest the young dog, when he grows up, should cut down the woods, and leave no groves for widows to take their lonesome solace in. The Wem estate, of course, can only devolve on him in case of your brother leaving no male issue.

" Well, my blessing and Heaven's be upon him, and make him like his father, with something of a better temper and a smoother head of hair; and then all the men and women must love him.

" Martin and the card-boys join in congratulations. Love to Sarah. Sorry we are not within caudle-shot.

"C. LAMB."

A few months after the child's birth the Hazlitts came to live in London.

CHAPTER VI

HAZLITT was thirty-four years of age when he first settled in London to earn a living for himself and his family. Hitherto he had led, though not a cloistered, yet a solitary life, free from responsibility, and he had been for the most part at liberty to chew the cud of his own thoughts, to direct the course of his own studies, and to write as much or as little as he liked. His good old father at Wem and his good-natured brother in Great Russell Street were always glad to see him and give him board and lodging in exchange for his society. Although already an author in 1812, except for his "Character of Pitt," which was inspired by, not to say borrowed from, Coleridge, some spirited notes to his compilation of speeches, and a flutter of the wing in his *Reply to Malthus* and in his Preface to Tucker, he had written nothing in the style and manner now soon to be known as his.

He was not at any time a man of many friendships. His manners were not good, his temper had become uncertain, and despite his sentiment he had not a warm heart. If any one insisted upon shaking hands with him, he held out something (so Leigh Hunt complained) like the fin of a fish. His political opinions were decidedly unpopular; for though he had never shared the rhapsodical dreams of Coleridge, the ex-

travagant hopes of Wordsworth, or the petulant sedi-
tion of Southey and Landor, he had rejoiced with a
fierce joy over the disgrace of the Bourbons, and

> " When to whelm the disenchanted nation,
>   Like fiends embattled by a wizard's wand,
>   The monarchs marched in evil day
>   And Britain joined the dire array,"

Hazlitt was darkly furious. On no one's eyes did the
beams of " the sun of Austerlitz " pour more resistless
day; and when that sun for ever set, his heart was
near breaking. Talfourd tells us how Hazlitt staggered under the blow of Waterloo; for he had accepted
Bonaparte not merely as the Child of the Revolution,
but as the Champion of Freedom ; and to him the Holy
Alliance was a conspiracy of stupid monarchs against
the abstract rights of the people, and Hazlitt never
found it difficult to connect a cause with a person.
He had followed Bonaparte's career "like a lover,"
had watched him trample on the pride of old royal
houses with malicious glee. To witness his disgrace
and captivity wrought "like madness in the brain."
Nor was his temper improved by being condemned to
witness the somewhat smug recantations of Wordsworth, Coleridge, Southey, and a host of lesser men,
who having indulged in vagaries of opinion and violence of revolutionary language far transcending any
of his, were now to be heard like a congregation of
rooks cawing round the old steeple. He exclaims in
a splenetic note to his essay on " Patronage and Puffing ": " I have endured all this marching and counter-
marching of poets and philosophers over my head as
well as I could ' like the camomile that thrives the

more 'tis trodden upon.' By Heavens! I think I'll endure it no more."

A man of Hazlitt's temper and opinions, and with the gifts of expression now discovered to be his, was not likely to live at peace with his fellow-men, *circa* 1812–1820.

He began peacefully enough by setting up his establishment in No. 19 York Street, Westminster, then a comfortable red-brick house with a small garden in front, and one of the numerous London residences of John Milton.

In 19 York Street Milton lived for six memorable years from 1652 to 1658. Here his first wife died, likewise his "late espoused saint"; here he became totally blind; here he wrote his Second Defence, *pro populo Anglicano*, perhaps the best example of that prose style that prompted Landor's remark that there was as much poetry in Milton's prose as there was prose in Wordsworth's poetry; here also he composed that "soul-animating strain," his sonnet on *The Late Massacre in Piedmont*, and five other of his sonnets, including the one to the "Memory of his Second Wife"; here also he began *Paradise Lost ;* and here he remained until the Restoration led him to lie hid for a season in Bartholomew Close, nor did he after the Act of Oblivion and Indemnity return to York Street.

In Hazlitt's time the house was the property of that tough old Reformer, Jeremy Bentham, who lived in a mansion with a large garden just behind. The door of No. 19 opened into a square hall or kitchen, and Hazlitt occupied as his own a big wainscoted room, reputed to be the poet's, upstairs, with two windows overlooking the old philosopher's garden. Hazlitt, finding that none of his neighbours knew or cared anything about Milton, recorded the fact that the poet had lived there on a tablet placed over the front door — an act of piety and devotion then rare.

Hazlitt's first bit of work in London was to deliver a course of lectures at the Russell Institution in Bloomsbury, not on the poets, but on the philosophers, his subject being "The Rise and Progress of Modern Philosophy, containing an Historical and Critical Account of the Principal Writers who have treated on Moral and Metaphysical Subjects from the time of Lord Bacon to the Present Day." The course consisted of ten lectures, of which large fragments remain, and may be read in the first volume of *The Literary Remains* (1836).

In the lecture on Hobbes, Hazlitt referred to a prospectus he had prepared of a history of a philosophy. Who attended these lectures or any of them is not known, but they were well worth listening to. Coleridge had set the fashion of lecturing, and was at this very date, January 1812, finishing a course on Shakespeare and Milton, which had been attended by as many as one hundred and fifty people at a time! Hazlitt began on the 14th of January, and made it his business to combat modern philosophy, by which, as he understood it, all thought is resolved into sensation, all morality into the love of pleasure, and all actions into mechanical impulse. "These three propositions taken together embrace almost every question relating to the human mind, and in their different ramifications and intersections form a net not unlike that used by the enchanters of old, which whosoever has once thrown over him will find all his efforts to

escape vain, and his attempts to reason freely on any
subject in which his own nature is concerned baffled
and confounded in every direction."

For Hobbes and Berkeley, as well as for Bishop
Butler's *Sermons* (not the *Analogy*), Hazlitt had great
reverence, despite strong differences of opinion. Of
Locke he had been taught by Coleridge to speak dis-
respectfully as a timid plagiarist from Hobbes, an
accommodator of truth to the spirit of the age, an intolerable thing in a metaphysician, however prudent
in a legislator.

I must not enter these fields, though I should like
to give a *précis* of Hazlitt's lecture on " Liberty and
Necessity," were it only to remind a babyish age of
the grandeur of the controversies that once engaged
the attention of philosophers and theologians. Over the
philosophical doctrine of Necessity a lurid light has
been thrown by the Augustinian theology. Its pale
crest of thought is reddened by the fires of hell, but
with this side issue Hazlitt had no concern. No such
précis shall be given; but in order to supply an illustration of Hazlitt's method and style, and at the same
time to pay a vicarious homage to a favourite author,
I will transcribe a single passage, and then hurry on
to where Poetry and the Drama,

> " Knit with the Graces and the Hours, in dance
> Lead on the Eternal Spring."

" To return to the doctrine of Necessity. I shall refer to
the authority of but one more writer, who has indeed ex-
hausted the subject, and anticipated what few remarks I had
to offer upon it. I mean Jonathan Edwards, in his treatise
on the Will. This work, setting aside its Calvinistic ten-

dency, with which I have nothing to do, is one of the most closely reasoned, elaborate, acute, serious, and sensible among modern productions. No metaphysician can read it without feeling a wish to have been the author of it. The gravity of the matter and the earnestness of the manner are alike admirable. His reasoning is not of that kind, which consists in having a smart answer for every trite objection, but in attaining true and satisfactory solutions of things perceived in all their difficulty and in all their force, and in every variety of connection. He evidently writes to satisfy his own mind and the minds of those who, like himself, are intent upon the pursuit of truth for its own sake. There is not an evasion or ambiguity in his whole book, nor a wish to produce any but thorough conviction. He does not therefore lead his readers into a labyrinth of words, or entangle them among the forms of logic, or mount the airy heights of abstraction, but descends into the plain, and mingles with the business and feelings of mankind, and grapples with common-sense, and subdues it to the force of true reason. All philosophy depends no less on deep and real feeling than on power of thought. I happen to have Edwards' 'Inquiry concerning Freewill' and Dr. Priestley's 'Illustrations of Philosophical Necessity' bound up in the same volume; and I confess that the difference in the manner of these two writers is rather striking. The plodding, persevering, scrupulous accuracy of the one, and the easy, cavalier, verbal fluency of the other, form a complete contrast. Dr. Priestley's whole aim seems be to evade the difficulties of his subject, Edwards' to answer them. The one is employed, according to Berkeley's allegory, in flinging dust in the eyes of his adversaries, while the other is taking true pains in digging into the mine of knowledge. All Dr. Priestley's arguments on this subject are mere hackneyed commonplaces. He had in reality no opinions of his own; and truth, I conceive, never takes very deep root in those minds on which it is merely engrafted. He uniformly adopted the vantage ground of every question, and borrowed those arguments which he found most easy to be wielded, and of most service in that kind of busy intellectual war-

fare to which he was habituated.   He was an able con-
troversialist, not a philosophical reasoner."

These lectures over, and there being no living to be
got out of "Divine Philosophy," Hazlitt descended
from the sublime to the (comparatively) ridiculous;
from Hobbes and Berkeley to Castlereagh and Burdett,
for he went as a reporter to the gallery of the House
of Commons.   He at once, the fact cannot be too
early or too bluntly stated, took to drink; but soon
becoming aware of the devastation wrought by this
evil habit, like another, earlier, and greater Parliamentary reporter, he altogether eschewed fermented
liquors, and remained for the rest of his days a rigid
total abstainer, only one lapse (was ever conversion so
complete?) being recorded against him.   His tea was
always of the strongest, it is true, and completely
ruined his digestion, but his "abstinence" was complete.   In the matter of strong drink no man is in a
position to throw a stone at Hazlitt.

> "Ye Prudes in Virtue, say,
>   Say, ye severest, what would you have done?"[1]

The House of Commons made a great impression
upon Hazlitt, and the experience he gained in the gallery enriches many of his essays.   He was no slavish
stenographer — no *verbatim* man; for though he had
been taught shorthand as well as Hebrew at Hackney,
he had forgotten both.   He listened to the speeches
with the ear of a connoisseur in rhetoric, and he fixed

---

[1] There is some uncertainty *when* Hazlitt first eschewed strong
drink, though none as to the fact that he long did so. See Procter's *Charles Lamb*, p. 27.

upon the orator the eye of a portrait painter, and afterwards at his leisure reproduced such portions of their
speeches as remained in his memory.　How completely
he entered into the spirit of the House of Commons,
and how well he knew the conditions of ´oratorical
success in that assembly, it would be easy to illustrate
by many quotations, but I must limit myself to one : —

"An orator can hardly get beyond *commonplaces;* if he
does, he gets beyond his hearers.　The most successful
speakers, even in the House of Commons, have not been the
best scholars or the finest writers, neither those who took
the most profound views of their subject, nor who adorned it
with the most original fancy or the richest combinations of
language.　Those speeches that in general told best at the
time are not now readable.　What were the materials of
which they were chiefly composed?　An imposing detail of
passing events, a formal display of official documents, an
appeal to established maxims, an echo of popular clamour,
some worn-out metaphor newly vamped up ;　some hackneyed
argument used for the hundredth, nay, thousandth time, to
fall in with the interests, the passions, or prejudices of listening and devoted admirers ;　some truth or falsehood, repeated
as the shibboleth of party time out of mind, which gathers
strength from sympathy as it spreads, because it is understood or assented to by the million, and finds, in the increased action of the minds of numbers, the weight and force
of an instinct. . . .　To give a reason for anything is to
breed a doubt of it, which doubt you may not remove in the
sequel ; either because your reason may not be a good one,
or because the person to whom it is addressed may not be
able to comprehend it, or because *others* may not be able to
comprehend it.　He who offers to go into the grounds of an
acknowledged axiom risks the unanimity of the company
' by most admired disorder,' as he who digs to the foundation
of a building to show its solidity risks its falling.　But a
commonplace is enshrined in its own unquestioned evidence,
and constitutes its own immortal basis.　Nature, it has been

said, abhors a *vacuum ;* and the House of Commons, it might be said, hates everything but a commonplace ! " — *Plain Speaker* " On the Difference between Writing and Speaking."

Lest, however, it should be supposed Hazlitt was only bored in the gallery, I add another quotation from the same essay : —

" The excitement of leading the House of Commons (which, in addition to the immediate attention and applause that follows, is a sort of whispering gallery to all Europe) must act upon the brain like brandy or laudanum upon the stomach ; and must, in most cases, produce the same debilitating effects afterwards. That any one accustomed all his life to the tributary roar of applause from the great council of the nation should think of dieting himself with the prospect of posthumous fame as an author, is like offering a confirmed dram-drinker a glass of fair water for his morning's draught."

Of all the speeches Hazlitt heard from the gallery, one made by Plunkett on the Catholic Question struck him as far the best. Tradition says Hazlitt was so excited by it that he quite forgot he was in the gallery for a purpose, and sat motionless and entranced. He admits that Plunkett was very indifferently reported ; but adds, with the composure of a philosopher employed at so much a week to take down the words of ordinary mortals, " though the best speeches are the worst reported, the worst are made better than they are, and so both find a convenient newspaper level."

Hazlitt very wisely did not remain long in the gallery, but found other employment in the *Morning Chronicle,* of which Mr. Perry, the father of Sir Erskine Perry and of the Miss Perrys, beloved of Thackeray, was editor and proprietor.

It was Perry's ill-luck to have two or three men of
genius on his staff, and he has suffered accordingly.
Between the brains and the capital of a newspaper
the relations are usually strained. Mr. Perry, so
Hazlitt thought, was unmindful of the countless columns of wit and wisdom contributed to an otherwise
dull organ of public opinion by his now ready pen.
On the other hand, the proprietor had his grievances.
" Poor Perry," writes Hazlitt, " what bitter complaints
he used to make that by running amuck against lords
and Scotchmen I should not leave him a place to dine
out at ! The expression of his face at these moments
as if he were shortly to be without a friend in the
world was truly pathetic." The humdrum is the
safest style. A man of genius and biting tongue is as
awkward a colleague on a newspaper as on the Treas-
ury Bench.

Hazlitt descended from the gallery of the House of
Commons to the pit of the theatre, and became dramatic critic for the *Chronicle* in October 1813, and continued to write regularly in that capacity until May
1814. He also wrote political articles for the same
paper. Specimens of his activity in both these directions will be found in his *View of the English Stage*
(1818) and in the *Political Essays* (1819).

After leaving the *Chronicle* Hazlitt wrote for the
Examiner both dramatic and literary pieces. The
essays we now read in the *Round Table* (1817) for the
most part appeared in the *Examiner*, where also were
published two savage notices of Southey's *Lay of the
Laureate*, which did not fail to attract the attention of
the *Quarterly Review*. Hazlitt became a man marked
out for insult.

As Hazlitt practically left off regular dramatic criticism in 1819, his performances in that direction fall first to be considered.

The best advice ever given to players was bestowed by Shakespeare in the famous passage in *Hamlet*, but who is to advise playgoers ?   An actor, like any other artist, is usually in his early stages willing to learn, but the public is seldom in a mood to be taught.   The poor wretch thinks it knows, and as a consequence is always ready to applaud players who have neither the accent of Christians, nor the gait of Christian, pagan, nor man, but who can strut and bellow and tear a passion to tatters.   Shakespeare, says Mr. Lewes in his book on *Actors and Acting* (1875), "saw the public mistaking violence for passion, turbulence for art, and he bade them remember the purpose of playing, which is to hold the mirror up to Nature."   But not only do players need advice, encouragement, and reproof, and playgoers the discipline of education and the crucifixion of the natural man ; but playwrights, those most sensitive of authors, usually require to be reminded of many things.   To be a good, sensible, dramatic critic of players, playgoers, and playwrights is a heavy task.

Hazlitt was in no sense a child of the greenroom. He was born in the study. He knew no players except (he says) Liston, nor was he, until he became a critic of the play, a very regular playgoer.[1] Like most sensible men, he went to the playhouse when it was convenient to do so.   In 1796 he first saw John Kemble in *Coriolanus*, and fell in love with the stately bearing

---

[1] "That was indeed going to the play when I went twice a year and had not been more than half-a-dozen times in my life." — From the *Letter-Bell* in *Sketches and Essays* (1839).

and scholarly manner of that old campaigner. *The
School for Scandal* was one of the chief delights of his
early days. " Jack Palmer was the man for Joseph
Surface. With what an air he trod the stage ! "
" Nobody was fit to succeed Palmer." We all have
our Jack Palmers. Of Mrs. Siddons, Hazlitt always
wrote in an ecstasy of passion. She was to him on the
mimic stage what Bonaparte was on the real stage.
" The stateliest ornament of the public mind, she not
only was the idol of the people, not only hushed the
shout of the pit in breathless expectation; but to the
retired and lonely student through long years of solitude her face shone as if an eye had appeared in heaven.
To have seen Mrs. Siddons was an event in every one's
life. . . . While the stage lasts there will never be
another Mrs. Siddons. Tragedy seemed to set with
her. It is pride and happiness enough for us to have
lived at the same time with her and one person more."

Hazlitt brought to his task-work, enthusiasm, eloquence, a considerable stock of miscellaneous reading,
and a liking for the play. " We do not much like any
persons who do not like plays." Hazlitt, it is to be
feared, was never sorry for a reason for disliking
" persons." It has often been said that his liking for
plays was three parts bookish. He preferred the
words to the action, an eloquent passage to the most
superb pantomime. He pronounces Shakespeare to be
too great for the stage, and bluntly declares that he
would never go to see a play of Shakespeare acted if
he could help it, his " most exquisite reason " being
that " not only are the more refined poetical beauties,
the minuter strokes of character, lost to the audience,
but the most striking and impressive passages, those

which having once read we can never forget, fail comparatively of their effect except in one or two instances." This cannot be good dramatic criticism, and would have made Shakespeare stare. Mr. John Forster, who was by the cabman's report "a very harbitrary gent," has gone so far as to affirm positively and in the teeth of Landor, Lamb, and Hazlitt, that the author of *Lear* " would rather have seen his play acted, however wretchedly, in a barn than heard it read to perfection in a palace." The barn might have amused, but the " Shakespearean Reading " in the palace must have bored Shakespeare well nigh to death.

Talfourd's remark that "the players put Hazlitt out " is often quoted, and cannot be disregarded. It probably meant no more than that the critic got easily tired of stage niceties and "business," and preferred pursuing his own thoughts and snuffing the perfume of his own sentimental memories to keeping his attention fixed upon the exits and entrances of the company. If seeing Hazlitt's favourite Kean was like reading Shakespeare by flashes of lightning, so reading Hazlitt's criticism of Kean is like seeing that actor by flashes of lightning. The gaps Hazlitt filled up out of his own head.

I expect, it is true, that fond as Hazlitt may have been of the play, he enjoyed old plays and old play-bills far more than he did turning out to go to Drury Lane to write a column and a half even about Kean. His was a literary, not a dramatic gusto.

" If, indeed, by any spell or power of necromancy, all the celebrated actors, for the last hundred years, could be made to appear again on the boards of Covent Garden and Drury Lane for the last time, in their most brilliant parts, what a rich treat to the town, what a feast for the critics, to go and see Betterton, and Booth, and Wilks, and Sandford, and Nokes, and Leigh, and Penkethman, and Bullock, and Estcourt, and Dogget, and Mrs. Barry, and Mrs. Montfort, and Mrs. Oldfield, and Mrs. Bracegirdle, and Mrs. Cibber, and Cibber himself, the prince of coxcombs, and Macklin, and Quin, and Rich, and Mrs. Clive, and Mrs. Pritchard, and Mrs. Abingdon, and Weston, and Shuter, and Garrick, and all the rest of those who 'gladdened life, and whose death eclipsed the gaiety of nations'! We should certainly be there. We should buy a ticket for the season. We should enjoy *our hundred days* again. We should not miss a single night. We would not, for a great deal, be absent from Betterton's Hamlet or his Brutus, or from Booth's Cato, as it was first acted to the contending applause of Whigs and Tories. We should be in the first row when Mrs. Barry (who was kept by Lord Rochester, and with whom Otway was in love) played Monimia or Belvidera ; and we suppose we should go to see Mrs. Bracegirdle (with whom all the world was in love) in all her parts. We should then know exactly whether Penkethman's manner of picking a chicken, and Bullock's mode of devouring asparagus, answered to the ingenious account of them in the *Tatler ;* and whether Dogget was equal to Dowton ; whether Mrs. Montford or Mrs. Abingdon was the finest lady ; whether Wilks or Cibber was the best Sir Henry Wildair ; whether Macklin was really 'the Jew that Shakespeare drew' ; and whether Garrick was, upon the whole, so great an actor as the world would have made him out ! Many people have a strong desire to pry into the secrets of futurity ; but for our own parts, we should be satisfied if we had the power to recall the dead, and live the past over again, as often as we pleased ! " — Criticisms of the English stage, *On Actors and Acting.*

Hazlitt's name as a dramatic critic is linked with Edmund Kean's, "the little man in a great passion," as his enemies called him. Hazlitt was in Drury Lane on the 26th of January 1814, when "Mr. Kean from the Theatre Royal, Exeter," assumed the part of Shylock, and the criticism of Kean's Shylock appeared in the *Morning Chronicle* the next day. Eighty-seven years have taken the fire out of Hazlitt's first notice of Kean; but followed up as that notice was by other criticisms of the same great actor's Hamlet, Othello, Iago, Macbeth, and Richard the Third, parts which, according to the happy practice of the time, succeeded one another with exciting and stimulating rapidity, Hazlitt's praise produced a great impression, and gave rise to the report, absolutely without foundation, that the critic had received £1500 from the management of Drury Lane to puff Kean.

Hazlitt had been told by his editor to give Kean as favourable a notice as he could, and he gave a true one. He rejoiced over Kean as the first gleam of genius thrown across the stage for many a long day. He found in him, for all his faults and shortcomings, a great actor, and he said so over and over again. His praise was discriminating. He was, I need not say, no stage-struck admirer, no fatuous, foolish-faced devotee, like those of old to whom

"Pritchard's genteel and Garrick six feet high."

To Hazlitt Kean did not cease to be a little man with a hoarse voice simply because he could act Othello, nor did he find it necessary to belittle Kemble because in certain parts and in certain ways he preferred Kean. Mr. Lewes, who used to see Kean between the years 1825 and 1832, agrees with Hazlitt in thinking Othello his greatest part. Lewes, like Hazlitt, was a great admirer, and accounted Kean, when measured by his strongest part, as incomparably the greatest actor he had ever seen. Both critics refer with delight to his acting of the scene with Anne in Richard the Third — to both Kean was a happy life-long memory. What nonsense it is about Shakespeare not being an acting dramatist! Kean's Romeo did not excite Hazlitt's admiration. "We never saw anything less ardent or less voluptuous. In the balcony scene, in particular, he was cold, tame, and unimpres-sive. It was said of Garrick and Barry in this scene that the one acted as if he would jump up to the lady, and the other as if he would make the lady jump down to him. Mr. Kean produced neither of these effects. He stood like a statue of lead."

Hazlitt collected his dramatic criticisms, and made a volume of them in 1818; but before that date he had turned them to considerable use in preparing for the press his well-known book, the *Characters of Shakespear's Plays* (1817). This work is not usually connected with Hazlitt's stage criticisms; but no inconsiderable part of it, and that part the best, consists of extracts bodily uplifted from the *Chronicle*, the *Champion*, and the *Examiner*. It is only necessary to compare the Mac-beth of the *Characters* with the criticism of Mr. Kean's Macbeth that appeared in the *Champion* of November 13, 1814; the Othello of the *Characters* with the criti-cism of Mr. Kean's Othello that appeared in the *Examiner* of July 24, 1814, and January 7, 1816; the Coriolanus of the *Characters* with the criticism of Mr. Kemble's Coriolanus that appeared in the *Examiner* of December 15, 1816; and to do the same with the Hamlet and Midsummer's Night's Dream of the *Characters* with the *Chronicle* of March 14, 1814, and the *Examiner* of January 21, 1816, to see clearly that but for the newspapers and Kean, Hazlitt would never have written his *Characters*.

Another noticeable thing is, how like a *Criticism* is to a *Character*, and how like a *Character* to a *Criticism*. Whether Hazlitt is criticising Shakespeare in his study, or from a side-box in the theatre, hardly makes any difference.

The obvious origin of the *Characters* explains a main defect. Hazlitt seldom gets away from the play in which the character he is discussing occurs; there are few side-lights, cross-quotations; he does not compare one character in one play with another in another play, but sticks to the " book of the play " more closely than there was any need for a literary critic to to do. When criticising a play as acted, why, then, the play is the thing; but when writing at large about Shakespeare and his men and women, you may surely roam freely through his whole spacious domain. If there is too much of the library in Hazlitt's theatre, so perhaps there is a little too much of the theatre in Hazlitt's library.

He did not confine himself during the years 1814–1816 to dramatic criticism; he wrote *de omnibus rebus* in the pages of the *Examiner ;* and in 1817 the *Round Table* appeared, containing fifty-two essays, all but twelve being Hazlitt's. The *Examiner* belonged to Leigh Hunt, whose original plan was that there should appear in it a series of papers in the manner of the *Spectator* and the *Tatler* by divers hands. Hence the title given to the series as it appeared in the columns of the paper. But Bonaparte's activity, so Hazlitt declares, broke up the *Round Table ;* Hunt, who wrote the dozen papers that were not Hazlitt's, busied himself in other ways; no third pen was found ready, and the task of keeping up the *Round Table* fell chiefly upon Hazlitt.

In these two volumes we first meet with Hazlitt, the miscellaneous writer. Montaigne was in Hazlitt's opinion the first person who in his essays led the way to this kind of writing among the moderns, being, according to Hazlitt, the first who had the courage to say as an author what he felt as a man. Hazlitt had plenty of this kind of courage — put a pen in his hand, and he would say anything. In the *Round Table* he applies his mind to subjects so varied as the " Causes of Methodism" and "John Buncle," and to abstract themes such as "The Tendency of Sects" and "Posthumous Fame," and the analysis of character.

For writing of this kind Hazlitt had many qualifications; he is never priggish, and seldom even for a moment dull; his fits of ill-temper and spleen are conveyed with a petulance that is never unpleasant; whilst he is always full, perhaps to overflowing, of human nature and the love of things. "Give a man," he says in "The Fight," "a topic in his head, a throb of pleasure in his heart, and he will be glad to share it with the first person he meets." In this sentence you may see Hazlitt, the miscellaneous writer, the horror of landladies, so prone was he to scribble topics for essays in blacklead on their walls and mantelpieces. When he found his topic, his heart throbbed, and still throbs, in a dozen volumes — " A tall English yeoman " — I have still " The Fight " open before me — " was making such a prodigious noise about rent and taxes and the price of corn now and formerly that

he had prevented us being heard at the gate. The
first thing I heard him say was to a shuffling person
who wanted to be off a bet for a shilling glass of
brandy and water, 'Confound it, man — don't be
insipid.' Thinks I, that is a good phrase." From
insipidity, the curse of the miscellaneous writer,
Hazlitt is wholly delivered.

These *Round Table* papers appeared in the *Examiner*
between January 1815 and January 1817. Hazlitt
never wrote better in his life. It was unfortunate
that when he came to reprint these essays, he thought
fit to include among them the "Character of Pitt,"
taken from Coleridge, and already part of his *Free
Thoughts* pamphlet of 1806. An author who at last
gets a hearing is tempted to force the public to listen
to what it once refused to hear. How Gifford fell
upon the *Round Table* has been already told, nor did
the *Characters of Shakespear's Plays* escape the same
foul-mouthed condemnation. The readers of the
Quarterly Review were told that Hazlitt in composing
his *Characters* disgraced literature, and proved that
his knowledge of Shakespeare and the English language was cn a par with the purity of his morals and
the depth of his understanding. This diatribe is pro-
fessedly based on some remarks upon "Coriolanus"
which had first done duty in the *Examiner* as a criticism of Mr. Kemble in that character, and were afterwards used afresh in the *Characters*, but the ferocity of
Gifford was entirely due to the fact that he regarded
Hazlitt as a sour Jacobinical fellow who was against
the Government. Had he written hymns, the same
measure would have been meted out to him. Gifford's
abuse stopped the sale of the *Characters* ; but, happily,

there is no need to grow tearful over Hazlitt's wrongs.
He had enough bile in his hold to swamp a dozen
Giffords, of whom he was to speak his mind both in
his *Letter to William Gifford, Esq.* (1819), and in his
Spirit of the Age (1825).

CHAPTER VII

HAVING seen Hazlitt fairly matriculated in the school, to use his own bitter words, of "squint-eyed suspicion, idiot wonder, and grinning scorn," it will be as well to return for a short while to his life, as he led it, apart from his manifold scribblings in the press. We left him sitting in Milton's wainscoted room on the first floor of No. 19 York Street, out of the windows of which he could see his landlord, old Jeremy Bentham, skipping about his garden "in eager conversation with some opposition member, some expatriated patriot or transatlantic adventurer, urging the extinction of close boroughs, or planning a code of laws for some 'lone island in the watery waste,' his walk almost amounting to a run, his tongue keeping pace with it in shrill, clattering accents, negligent of his person, his dress, and his manners, intent only on his grand theme of Utility." [1] Hazlitt is as good a hand at a description as Carlyle himself.

Unluckily, the marriage with Miss Stoddart did not turn out a success. It would have been strange if it had. Neither party had bargained for happiness. It was not a case of love flying out of the window, for the love was never there. Mrs. Hazlitt was unromantic, undomestic, untidy, and selfish, and her husband

[1] 'Jeremy Bentham.' — *The Spirit of the Age.*

115

was a sentimentalist on paper, irregular in habits, uncertain in temper, and at least as selfish as his spouse. The result was uncomfortable. The couple had neither money, manners, nor love to keep them together. With Gifford ravening like a wolf in Albemarle Street, and Bonaparte shut up with Sir Hudson Lowe in Longwood, it would have been a consolatory circumstance had there been an Angel in the house in York Street. Charles Churchill is not a sincere poet, but his lines ring true : —

> " 'Tis not the babbling of a busy world,
>   Where praise and censure are at random hurled,
>   Which can the meanest of my thoughts control,
>   Or shake one settled purpose of my soul ;
>   Free and at large might their wild curses roam
>   If all, if all, alas ! were well at home."

All was not well at home, but the Hazlitts got on at least as well as might be expected. They never laid hands on each other, and indeed remained through the very oddest occurrences good friends enough. Their little boy was a source of pleasure and a comfort to both his parents. Haydon, whose acquaintance Hazlitt made in Northcote's studio, has recorded in his diary how he once went by invitation to York Street to attend the somewhat delayed christening of the young William, now a boy three years old. On arriving at the door Haydon found Hazlitt out, and no signs of any impending rite. Mrs. Hazlitt was in a bedgown and low spirits, and said that her husband had gone out to look for a parson. Haydon went in search and found the father in St. James's Park in a great rage, all the parsons being away from home. The ceremony had to be postponed, but later in the afternoon Charles Lamb and his sister arrived, and one or two others, and there was good talk, but no food. The boy was duly christened (I hasten to add) in St. Margaret's Church on the 26th of September 1814.

Mrs. Hazlitt had good cause for her low spirits and indifferent health, as may be found stated with unusual bluntness in her grandson's *Memoirs of William Hazlitt* (1867). Another son, christened John, was born in 1815, but, to his father's lasting sorrow, died before he had lived a year.

Although Hazlitt was not a man famous for his friendships, he was a good hand at making acquaintances. He was excellent company on the top of a stage-coach or in the parlour of an old inn. He had no passion for respectability, and did not insist on genius. He was not fond of parties; and though he looked well on his way to Mr. Curran's " in black silk smalls and blue coat and gilt buttons," he did not willingly wear such clothes. The Bloomsbury grandeur of the Montagus did not impress him. He preferred the company of any Mr. John Simpkins, " hosier in the Strand," or of Mr. Fisher, " the poulterer in Duke Street," who, wiser than Lamb, could enjoy both *Gil Blas* and *Don Quixote*, and doted on Sterne, to that of dull members of Parliament, or of authors in love with themselves. His essays are full of references to odd acquaintances whose society and characteristic, if not profound, remarks tickled his fancy:[1] " One of the most pleasant and least tiresome

---

[1] " I know an undertaker that is the greatest prig in the streets of London, and an Aldermanbury haberdasher that has the most military strut of any lounger in Bond Street or St. James's." — Essay on *Fashion* in *Sketches and Essays* (1839).

of our acquaintance is a humourist who has three or four quaint witticisms and proverbial phrases which he always repeats over and over ; but he does this with the same vivacity and freshness as ever, so that you feel the same amusement with less effort than if he had startled his hearers with a succession of original conceits."

Mr. George Mounsey of Staple Inn, of the firm of Mounsey and Gray, Solicitors, lives in Hazlitt's Essay on Coffee-house Politicians, after the same, though not quite the same fashion, as does George Dyer in the Essays of Elia. Hazlitt never grew tired of Mounsey, though others speedily did. This excellent, though bibulous solicitor, was the oldest frequenter and longest sitter-up of the Southampton Coffee-house standing at the corner of Southampton Buildings and Chancery Lane.[1] Just the place for a solicitor. " I never knew Mounsey approve of anything unfair or illiberal. There is a candour and uprightness about his mind which can be neither wheedled or browbeat into unjustifiable complaisance. He looks straight forward as he sits with his glass in his hand, turning neither to the right nor to the left. . . . Mounsey without being the most communicative is the most conversible man I know. . . . If he has nothing to say, he drinks your health. . . . His favourite phrase is, ' We have all of us something of the coxcomb.' "

Mounsey in his day had consorted with wits. At least he said he knew Tobin, Porson, Wilson, Paley, Erskine, and others, and he could speak of the pleasantness of Paley and the potations and Greek of Porson. But of Greek in cider cellars Mounsey had

----

[1] He disappears from the Law Lists about 1832.

no great opinion; and on Hazlitt's saying that he once, and only once, saw Porson, and that was in the library of the London Institution in Finsbury Square, when he was dressed in an old rusty black coat with cobwebs hanging to the skirts of it, and with a large patch of brown paper covering the whole length of his nose, looking for all the world like a drunken carpenter, and talking to one of the proprietors with an air of suavity approaching condescension, Mounsey observed, " I submit, sir, whether common-sense is not the principal thing."

Another acquaintance was Joseph Parkes, also a solicitor, a Birmingham man, and the author, if I mistake not, of an exceedingly interesting, not to say exciting, *History of the Court of Chancery* composed in a spirit of rational reform which it has taken half a century partially to realise. Parkes had his lighter moments, which have secured him a fame which has already outlived the old Court he wrote about, for he figures in Hazlitt's famous " Fight " : " Joe and I, though we seldom met, were an *alter idem* on this memorable occasion, and had not an idea that we did not candidly impart ; and so carelessly did we fleet the time, that I wish no better when there is another fight than to have him for a companion on my journey down and to return with my friend Jack Pigott talking of what was to happen, or what did happen, with a noble subject always at hand, and liberty to digress to others whenever they offered."

What was the noble subject always at hand when in company with Jack Pigott? Had it been "Bob Pigott," "the Englishman of the French Revolution," the answer would be easy ; but Robert Pigott died in 1794.

Between Lamb and Hazlitt there was real friendship; and, in the true sense of a phrase now soiled by
ignoble use, mutual admiration. They quarrelled at
times — once, but not for long, over an early copy of
Wordsworth's *Excursion*, sent to Lamb for the purpose
of a review in the *Quarterly* of all places. Hazlitt
heard of its arrival, and sent Martin Burney to lay
hands on it, which Martin did, and brought it back to
Hazlitt, who at once sat himself down and wrote a
long and eloquent but independent critique, which was
forthwith printed in the *Examiner*, and afterwards reprinted in the *Round Table*, and all this before Lamb
had time to compose a sentence of his review for
the *Quarterly*, which when it did appear was so
mangled by the editor as to be worthless. Elia was
annoyed, and no wonder; and Hazlitt was so annoyed
at his being annoyed, that he called at the Temple and
gave Charles and his sister "a good blowing-up."
There are several references to this affair in Lamb's
letters to the Wordsworths. Afterwards a more serious
quarrel, about what I know not, separated the two
friends for too long a period; but Lamb's famous
letter to Southey, which appeared in the *London
Magazine* for October 1823, contained an allusion to
Hazlitt in terms which made a reconciliation inevitable.

A well-known essay of Hazlitt's is called "Persons
one would wish to have seen," and purports to be a
record of the talk at one of Lamb's "Wednesdays" in
the Temple. I do not think it is one of his happiest
efforts, and it is impossible to accept it as a specimen
of Lamb's mode of talk. Hazlitt had not the temperament of a Boswell, his disposition was too indolent,
his wit too quick, his historic conscience too sluggish,

to make him a trustworthy reporter of other men's talk.[1] His book on Northcote illustrates his method. It no doubt contains some of the things Northcote said; but how much should be Northcote, and how much Hazlitt, talking as if he were Northcote, was determined by the whim of the moment of writing.

A better account of Lamb and his friends is to be found in the essay *On the Conversation of Authors* : —

" This was the case formerly at Lamb's, where we used to have many lively skirmishes at their Thursday evening parties. O for the pen of John Buncle to consecrate a *petit souvenir* to their memory ! There was Lamb himself, the most delightful, the most provoking, the most witty and sensible of men. He always made the best pun and the best remark in the course of the evening. His serious conversation, like his serious writing, is his best. No one ever stammered out such fine, piquant, deep, eloquent things in half-a-dozen half sentences as he does. His jests scald like tears, and he probes a question with a play upon words. What a keen, laughing, hair-brained vein of home-felt truth ! What choice venom ! How often did we cut into the haunch of letters while we discussed the haunch of mutton on the table ! How we skimmed the cream of criticism ! How we got into the heart of controversy ! How we picked out the marrow of authors ! ' And, in our flowing cups, many a good name and true was freshly remembered.' Recollect (most sage and critical reader) that in all this I was but a guest ! Need I go over the names ? They were but the old everlasting set — Milton and Shakespeare, Pope and Dryden, Steele and Addison, Swift and Gay, Fielding, Smollett, Sterne, Richardson, Hogarth's prints, Claude's landscapes, the cartoons at Hampton Court, and all those things that, having once been, must ever be. The Scotch novels had not then been heard of; so we said nothing about them. In general, we were hard upon the moderns. The author of the *Rambler* was

---

[1] His memory was seldom at fault (see Lamb's 'Mystification,' before quoted), but he had no conscience in such matters.

only tolerated in Boswell's *Life* of him; and it was as much as any one could do to edge in a word for Junius. Lamb could not bear *Gil Blas*. This was a fault. I remember the greatest triumph I ever had was in persuading him, after some years' difficulty, that Fielding was better than Smollett. On one occasion he was for making out a list of persons famous in history that one would wish to see again—at the head of whom were Pontius Pilate, Sir Thomas Browne, and Dr. Faustus—but we blackballed most of his list! But with what a gusto would he describe his favourite authors, Donne, or Sir Philip Sidney, and call their most crabbed passages *delicious!* He tried them on his palate as epicures taste olives, and his observations had a smack in them, like a roughness on the tongue. With what discrimination he hinted a defect in what he admired most—as in saying that the display of the sumptuous banquet in *Paradise Regained* was not in true keeping, as the simplest fare was all that was necessary to tempt the extremity of hunger, and stating that Adam and Eve in *Paradise Lost* were too much like married people. He has furnished many a text for Coleridge to preach upon. There was no fuss or cant about him ; nor were his sweets or his sours ever diluted with one particle of affectation. I cannot say that the party at Lamb's were all of one description. There were honorary members, lay brothers. Wit and good fellowship was the motto inscribed over the door. When a stranger came in, it was not asked, 'Has he written any-thing?'—we were above that pedantry; but we waited to see what he could do. If he could take a hand at piquet, he was welcome to sit down. If a person liked anything, if he took snuff heartily, it was sufficient. He would understand by analogy the pungency of other things besides Irish black-guard or Scotch rappee. A character was good anywhere, in a room or on paper. But we abhorred insipidity, affectation, and fine gentlemen. There was one of our party who never failed to mark 'two for his Nob' at cribbage, and he was thought no mean person. This was Ned Phillips, and a better fellow in his way breathes not. There was Rickman, who asserted some incredible matter-of-fact as a likely para-dox, and settled all controversies by an *ipse dixit*, a *fiat* of

his will, hammering out many a hard theory on the anvil
of his brain — the Baron Munchausen of politics and practical
philosophy; there was Captain Burney, who had you at an
advantage by never understanding you; there was Jem White,
the author of *Falstaff's Letters*, who the other day left this
dull world to go in search of more kindred spirits, 'turning like
the latter end of a lover's lute'; there was Ayrton, who sometimes dropped in, the Will Honeycomb of our set; and Mrs.
Reynolds, who, being of a quiet turn, loved to hear a noisy
debate.   An utterly uninformed person might have supposed
this a scene of vulgar confusion and uproar.   While the
most critical question was pending, while the most difficult
problem in philosophy was solving, Phillips cried out, 'That's
game,' and Martin Burney muttered a quotation over the last
remains of a veal pie at a side-table.   Once, and once only,
the literary interest overcame the general.   For Coleridge was
riding the high German horse, and demonstrating the categories of the transcendental philosophy to the author of the
Road to Ruin; who insisted on his knowledge of German
and German metaphysics, having read the *Critique of Pure
Reason* in the original.   'My dear Mr. Holcroft,' said Coleridge, in a tone of infinitely provoking conciliation, 'you
really put me in mind of a sweet pretty German girl, about
fifteen, that I met with in the Hartz forest in Germany, and
who one day, as I was reading the *Limits of the Knowable
and the Unknowable*, the profoundest of all his works, with
great attention, came behind my chair, and leaning over, said,
"What, *you* read Kant? Why, *I* that am a German born
don't understand him!"' This was too much to bear; and
Holcroft, starting up, called out in no measured tone, 'Mr.
Coleridge, you are the most eloquent man I ever met with,
and the most troublesome with your eloquence!' Phillips
held the cribbage-peg that was to mark him game suspended
in his hand, and the whist table was silent for a moment.   I
saw Holcroft downstairs; and on coming to the landing-place
in Mitre Court, he stopped me to observe that 'he thought
Mr. Coleridge a very clever man, with a great command of
language, but that he feared he did not always affix very
precise ideas to the words he used.' After he was gone we

had our laugh out, and went on with the argument on the nature of Reason, and Imagination, and the Will. I wish I could find a publisher for it ; it would make a supplement to the *Biographia Literaria* in a volume and half octavo." [1]

Hazlitt's finances were never prosperous ; but though not a good accountant, he was a practical economist, his tastes being simple and his habits inexpensive, though two ounces at breakfast and two at tea-time of Souchong, at twelve shillings a pound, bought at Robinson's in Piccadilly, must have cost a good deal more by the end of the year than Lamb's porter. As a journalist and dramatic critic he earned a fair wage ; and from 1814 to the end of his life he was a regular, and until the advent of Macaulay, the most brilliant, contributor to the *Edinburgh Review*. Hardly any man is altogether free from the taint of respectability ; and there is something half touching, half ludicrous, in the pride Hazlitt always had in becoming and remaining a contributor to the "Blue and Buff," although, as a matter of fact, he wrote far better for Hunt's *Yellow Dwarf* than ever he did for Jeffrey in the *Edinburgh*.

His income from all sources was never large, five or six hundred a year at the most; and as Mrs. Hazlitt had no domestic gifts, it is not surprising to come across traces of distress and anxiety. The philosophic Bentham seems so far to have forgotten his abhorrence of attorneys and our absurd juridical system, as to put an execution for rent into Milton's house; and, when remonstrated with, to have excused himself by saying he had never heard of Hazlitt as an author, and regarded him only as a tenant. And yet the old

---

[1] ' On the Conversation of Authors.' — *The Plain Speaker*.

man had visited Leigh Hunt in prison; and finding
the author of *Rimini* playing battledore and shuttle-
cock with his jailer, not only watched the game with
interest, but at its close volunteered a practical reform
in the constitution of shuttlecocks, which struck the
jailer as excellent, and has remained unattended to
from that day to this.

But Hazlitt's money matters, like his domestic affairs,
might have been worse than they were. He was never
in prison for debt, or even inside a sponging-house, as
was Dr. Johnson.

His last work as a dramatic critic was done for the
Times, a paper which, though it abused Bonaparte,
managed to stroke Hazlitt the right way; for in his
preface to his *View of the English Stage* (1818) he advises
" any one who has an ambition to write, and to write
his best in the periodical press, to get, if he can, a position in the *Times* newspaper, the editor of which is a
man of business, and not a man of letters. He may
write there as long and as good articles as he can without being turned out for it."

This is handsomely put, though whether Hazlitt
meant to give pleasure to Mr. Walter, or pain to Mr.
Perry, it were rash to affirm.

Mr. Alsager, who was at this time the commercial
editor of the *Times*, was also on the Committee of the
Surrey Institution in the Blackfriars Road, Mr. P. G.
Patmore being the secretary. On Mr. Alsager's
introduction, Hazlitt proposed to the Committee to
deliver a course of lectures in the evening on the English Poets. The offer was accepted, and the lectures
delivered, and, proving successful, two other courses
followed, and the three courses form three volumes: —

I. Lectures on the English Poets. 1818.
II. Lectures on the English Comic Writers. 1819.
III. Lectures on the Dramatic Literature of the Age
    of Elizabeth. 1820.

These poetical lectures were better attended than
the metaphysical ones of 1812; but the number of
persons likely to turn out on January evenings to
hear a journalist, and the late dramatic critic of the
Chronicle, discourse on Shakespeare and Milton in the
Blackfriars Road, could never be large.   Coleridge was
again lecturing, sometimes on the very same evening,
in a small hall in Flower-de-luce Court, off Fetter Lane.
Two such lecturers at Coleridge and Hazlitt are not on
Major Pond's list, but the great world never gets the
best of anything — it always waits too long.

Mr. Patmore, in his *Friends and Acquaintances*
(1854), says he remembers walking home to York
Street with Hazlitt after the first lecture, and how
at first Hazlitt declined to take the proffered arm of
the secretary; but on its being pressed upon him,
took hold of it " as if it had been a bar of hot iron,
and fingered it gingerly."

Like most lecturers, Hazlitt had to put up as best
he could with his audiences.   The motives that prompt
men and women to go to lectures on winter nights
are varied, and include many which have nothing to
do with respect for the lecturer or interest in his
subject. Talfourd's account of the lectures is too
good to be omitted : —

"Mr. Hazlitt delivered three courses of lectures at the
Surrey Institution, to the matter of which we have repeatedly
alluded — on 'The English Poets,' on 'The English Comic

Writers,' and on 'The Age of Elizabeth' — before audiences
with whom he had but 'an imperfect sympathy.' They consisted chiefly of Dissenters, who agreed with him in his hatred
of Lord Castlereagh, but who 'loved no plays'; of Quakers,
who approved him as the opponent of Slavery and Capital
Punishment, but who 'heard no music'; of citizens, devoted
to the main chance, who had a hankering after 'the improvement of the mind,' but to whom his favourite doctrine
of its natural disinterestedness was a riddle; of a few enemies,
who came to sneer; and a few friends, who were eager to learn
and to admire. The comparative insensibility of the bulk of
his audience to his finest passages sometimes provoked him to
awaken their attention by points which broke the train of his
discourse, after which he could make himself amends by some
abrupt paradox which might set their prejudices on edge, and
make them fancy they were shocked. He startled many of
them at the onset by observing that since Jacob's dream
'the heavens have gone further off and become astronomical,'
a fine extravagance, which the ladies and gentlemen who had
grown astronomical themselves under the preceding lecturer
felt called on to resent as an attack on their severer studies.
When he read a well-known extract from Cowper, comparing
a poorer cottager with Voltaire, and had pronounced the line
'a truth the brilliant Frenchman never knew,' they broke into
a joyous shout of self-gratulation, that they were so much
wiser than a wicked Frenchman. When he passed by Mrs.
Hannah More with observing that 'she had written a great
deal which he had never read,' a voice gave expression to the
general commiseration and surprise by calling out, 'More pity
for you!' They were confounded at his reading, with more
emphasis perhaps than discretion, Gay's epigrammatic lines
on Sir Richard Blackmore, in which scriptural persons are
freely hitched into rhyme; but he went doggedly on to the
end, and, by his perseverance, baffled those who, if he acknowledged himself wrong by stopping, would have hissed him
without mercy. He once had an edifying advantage over
them. He was enumerating the humanities which endeared
Dr. Johnson to his mind; and at the close of an agreeable
catalogue mentioned, as last and noblest, 'his carrying the

poor victim of disease and dissipation on his back through Fleet Street,' at which a titter arose from some, who were struck by the picture as ludicrous, and a murmur from others, who deemed the allusion unfit for ears polite. He paused for an instant, and then added in his sturdiest and most impressive manner, ' an act which realises the parable of the Good Samaritan,' at which his moral and delicate hearers shrank rebuked into deep silence. He was not eloquent in the true sense of the term ; for his thoughts were too weighty to be moved along by the shallow stream of feeling which an evening's excitement can rouse. He wrote all his lectures, and read them as they were written ; but his deep voice and earnest manner suited his matter well. He seemed to dig into his subject — and not in vain. In delivering his longer quotations, he had scarcely continuity enough for the versi-fication of Shakespeare and Milton, ' with linked sweetness long drawn out ' ; but he gave Pope's brilliant satire and divine compliments, which are usually complete within the couplet, with an elegance and point which the poet himself would have felt as their highest praise." [1]

Hazlitt had, however, one auditor who would have de-vulgarised Tammany Hall, for John Keats regu-larly attended the first course, and wrote: "Hazlitt's last was on Gray, Collins, Young, etc., and he gave a very fine piece of discriminating criticism on Swift, Voltaire, and Rabelais. I was very disappointed with his treatment of Chatterton." What Hazlitt had said about Chatterton was this: " He did not show extraor-dinary powers of genius, but extraordinary precoc-ity. Nor do I believe he would have written better had he lived. He knew this himself, or he would have lived." It is easy to understand this rough-fibred sentence, which smacks of Chelsea, falling harshly on the sensitive ear of Keats, who, with nothing yet done,

[1] See *Literary Remains*, I, cxxvii.

had but three feverish years to live, in which, however, he was to build for himself an immortality of fame.

These lectures of Hazlitt's must have had many students; for it is impossible to read them without noticing how firmly he has managed to imbed, or pot out, his ideas and opinions about the English poets into the clay of our compositions. To-day all ordinary, well-read, sensible people, the commonplace critics about whom Hazlitt wrote in the *Round Table* almost as amusingly as Dr. Johnson had done before him in the *Rambler*, entertain as their own the lecturer's opinions about Chaucer and Spenser, Gray and Collins, Swift and Goldsmith; but in 1818, when Dr. Darwin and Hayley were still preferred to Cowper and Burns, whilst Akenside (the favourite poet of Hannah More) and Young loomed large in the general mind, these opinions of Hazlitt's were very far from being "in widest commonalty spread."

Hazlitt's success in circulating his opinions is largely attributable to the fact that, like his sworn admirer in our own day, Mr. Bagehot, he has always been a favourite author with journalists and ready-writers. His views are infectious, his style attractive, and his words very quotable with or without acknowledgment. Indeed, it is very hard always to remember when you are quoting Hazlitt. No more original miscellaneous writer can easily be named than this same Mr. Bagehot, and yet he occasionally gives you half a page of Hazlitt without a word said about it. Compare Bagehot's description of Southey in his essay on "Shakespeare" (*Literary Studies*, i. 137) with Hazlitt's sketch of Southey in *The Spirit of the Age*, and what I mean will be made plain. Gracious rills from

the Hazlitt watershed have flowed in all directions,
fertilising a dry and thirsty land.   You can mark
their track as, to quote Cowper's beautiful lines about
real rills, they

> "lose themselves at length
> In matted grass that with a livelier green
> Betrays the secret of their silent course."

Hazlitt approached his task as a critic of poetry in
a manly spirit of appreciation. He liked poetry as
he liked Salisbury Plain and Mrs. Siddons and Titian
and Claude, for the pleasure it gave him and the good
it did him.   Poetry tickled his ear, excited his fancy,
moved his heart. He was not a regular student, original research was no more in his way than in Johnson's.   Indeed, he would have done better had he
taken more pains.

He was quite above the miserable affectation of pre-
tending to care only for poetry. He cared, as we
know, for a great many other things. "Poetry," he
says in his essay on "People with One Idea," "is a
very fine thing, but there are other things besides."
"I deny," he wrote in his preface to the *Political
Tracts*, "that liberty and slavery are convertible terms;
that right and wrong, truth and falsehood, plenty and
famine, the comforts or wretchedness of a people, are
matters of perfect indifference."   For Hazlitt, poetry
was no mere

> "Stretched metre of an antique song";

it was food for the mind, matter for the heart — something that helped him to go on living, thinking, loving,
and it must be added, hating. He loved Milton for his

republicanism at least as much as for his versification ; and he certainly would have found something to say for *Madoc* and the *Curse of Kehama* had not Southey deserted his first love and taken up with the false Duessa, that hateful Legitimacy, by which word Hazlitt always means the cause of those European kings with whose crowns Bonaparte had once played so glorious a game of bowls.

Fine literary folk who think a new play by Shakespeare would be cheaply purchased with the Bill of Rights will never be quite reconciled to Hazlitt.

In both poetry and prose Hazlitt's preferences were frankly avowed and his dislikes outspoken. He never hesitated to say as an author what he felt as a man. He belonged to no school or coterie. His knowledge and taste for poetry was increased and purified by his friendship with Lamb; and he had felt the stimulus of Coleridge in poetry as well as in metaphysics and politics, but he remained his own man — a solitary and independent figure. He liked Blair's *Grave* and Warton's Sonnets, and he said so. Sir Philip Sidney's *Arcadia* bored him to death, and he said so. Sir Thomas Browne's strained fancifulness and jargonised speech teased him, and he said so. On the other hand, what member of the Anglican Church has so bathed the name of Jeremy Taylor in the sunshine of eloquent appreciation as has this Jacobinical son of a Socinian preacher ?

In singling out Hazlitt's treatment of Swift for especial praise, Keats showed that recognition of the great merits of Swift's versification which the author of the *Ode to Autumn* shared with the author of *Œnone*. " There is not only," said Hazlitt, " a dry humour, an exquisite tone of irony in these productions [the *Imitations of Horace* and the Dean's verses on his own death], but there is a touching, unpretending pathos mixed up with the most whimsical and eccentric strokes of satire." Glorious John was wrong for once when he said, "Cousin Swift, you will never be a poet," but perhaps Dryden meant a poet "in the grand style."

Young, Hazlitt had the courage to dismiss as a gloomy epigrammatist who had abused great powers of thought and language. Of Young's powers of language there can be no doubt — he served his turn and stirred to the pitch of enthusiasm the boyish admiration of Edmund Burke. The genius of Collins, somewhat of a test case in 1818, Hazlitt proudly hails; and he puts him above Gray, his usual yoke-fellow in the publisher's harness, though Hazlitt was very glad to extol the merits of the *Elegy*, since it enabled him to have a sly dig at Wordsworth, who once undertook to show that the language of that famous piece is "unintelligible," yet, says Hazlitt dryly, "it has been understood." To Dryden, Hazlitt fails to do complete justice, but his Pope is perfect. Gay, he oddly prefers to Prior. Akenside, he banished in a sentence, which must have made many of his hearers very angry, for in liberal Nonconforming circles Akenside was long considered only second to Milton.

With our earlier poets Hazlitt had but a haphazard acquaintance. The poetry he had not read would fill many volumes. Donne's poems he evidently did not know; and though he displays his critical gift by his treatment of Marvell, he frankly admitted he had never read the "Ode upon Cromwell's Return from

Ireland," which contains the famous lines upon the death of the king.

For Drummond of Hawthornden, Suckling, and Wither he exhibits an unexpected tenderness, probably attributable to his spending an evening with Charles Lamb. The secret of Herrick's charm was never revealed to him.

For the Elizabethan dramatists other than Shakespeare, Hazlitt had no feeling, and with their writings but small familiarity. He shared Landor's indifference. Ben Jonson he could not but greatly admire, but he had made no study of his plays, which have been called works. Yet for all this, Hazlitt's introductory lecture to these dramatists is a splendid performance, and in one of the most perfunctory of the lectures he showed his fine poetic feeling by quoting from John Lyly's *Alexander and Campaspe* the Apelles song "Cupid and my Campaspe played."

It was probably Hazlitt's quotation that led to this superb lyric being included in Chambers's *Encyclopædia of English Literature*, a popular collection which did more in its day to instil good taste and the love of literature in the minds of young England and Scotland than Church, State, or University.

As for the four dramatists, Wycherley, Congreve, Vanbrugh, and Farquhar, Hazlitt is probably the last critic likely to be read who writes about their plays with a complete abandonment to their point of view. In 1818 the dramas of these distinguished wits, or some of them, still held the boards. "Munden's *Foresight*," wrote Hazlitt, "if it is not just the thing, is a wonderful rich and powerful piece of comic acting. His look is planet-struck, his dress and appear-

ance like one of the signs of the zodiac taken down.
Nothing can be more bewildered, and it only wants
a little more helplessness, a little more of the doating
querulous garrulity of the age, to be all that one con-
ceives of the superannuated, star-gazing original."
Munden in Congreve's *Foresight* evidently did not put
Hazlitt out.   This is true dramatic criticism.   Millamant in Congreve's *Way of the World* is one of Hazlitt's
many literary loves.   He describes her in detail, and
declares that he would rather have seen Mrs. Abingdon's Millamant than any Rosalind that ever appeared
on the stage.   Mrs. Abingdon he never saw ; but Mrs.
Jordan, who used to play Miss Prue in *Love for Love*,
Miss Peggy in *The Country Wife*, Miss Hoyden in the
Relapse, and Corinna in the *Confederacy*, he had seen
in all these parts, and never could make up his mind
which was best.   Hazlitt maintains that *Miss Peggy*
is a character that will live for ever, "so built is it
on first principles and brought out in the fullest
broadest manner."   He reminds us how Sir John
Brute in *The Provoked Wife* was one of Garrick's
favourite characters, and he dates the decline of
English comedy from the death of Farquhar in
1709.

It is very necessary to keep on one's guard against
the sham raptures of men of literary genius.   Great
gifts of expression always seeks employment; and if
writers so endowed wish to describe themselves as
basking in glorious sunshine, they will not be de-
terred from doing so by the fact that at the moment
of writing the rain is falling heavily to the ground.
It is Talfourd, I think, who advises Hazlitt's readers
"to allow for the wind."

But we are safe in assuming Hazlitt's enthusiasm
for these four worthies to be quite genuine, vouched
for as it is in a variety of ways. The reason why but
few people now living can share Hazlitt's intense enjoyment of these playwrights is not any failure to
appreciate their wit, or the consummate skill of their
dialogue, of which Sheridan's is often but a metallic
echo, nor is it any unconquerable aversion to the occasional coarseness of their speech or frivolity of their
tone — it is their heartlessness, or rather their stony-
heartedness, which dries up in us the capacity to take
any pleasure in their plays. *Love for Love* is perhaps
the wittiest play ever written ; but in the first scene
the wittiest character in it displays such sheer brutal-
ity and callosity as to make a modern sick and able to
read no more that day.

Hazlitt's lectures are animated, manly discourses,
full of substance and sense, and abounding in passages
of eloquence and fancy : —

"Many people suppose that poetry is something to be
found only in books, contained in lines of ten syllables, with
like endings ; but wherever there is a sense of beauty, or
power, or harmony, as in the motion of a wave of the sea,
in the growth of a flower, that 'spreads its sweet leaves
through the air, and dedicates its beauty to the sun,' *there*
is poetry. . . .

"The child is a poet, in fact, when he first plays at hide-
and-seek, or repeats the story of Jack the Giantkiller ; the
shepherd boy is a poet when he first crowns his mistress with
a garland of flowers ; the countryman when he stops to look
at the rainbow ; the city apprentice when he gazes after the
Lord Mayor's show ; the miser when he hugs his gold ; the
courtier who builds his hopes upon a smile ; the savage who
paints his idol with blood ; the slave who worships a tyrant,
or the tyrant who fancies himself a god ; the vain, the

ambitious, the proud, the choleric man, the hero and the
coward, the beggar and the king, the rich and the poor,
the young and the old, all live in a world of their own making; and the poet does no more than describe what all the
others think and act."

"Poetry is not a branch of authorship; it is the stuff of
which our life is made."

I will quote another passage which reminds me of a
corresponding passage in one of Dr. Newman's books,
and indeed the resemblance is often close between
these two animated authors: —

"The poet of nature is one who, from the elements of
beauty, of power, and of passion in his own breast, sympa-
thises with whatever is beautiful, and grand, and impassioned in nature, in its simple majesty, in its immediate
appeal to the senses, to the thoughts and hearts of all men ;
so that the poet of nature, by the truth, and depth, and
harmony of his mind, may be said to hold communion with
the very soul of nature; to be identified with, and to fore-
know, and to record, the feelings of all men, at all times
and places, as they are liable to the same impressions; and
to exert the same power over the minds of his readers that
nature does. He sees things in their eternal beauty, for he
sees them as they are; he feels them in their universal
interest, for he feels them as they affect the first principles
of his and our common nature. Such was Homer, such was
Shakespeare, whose works will last as long as nature, because they are a copy of the indestructible forms and everlasting impulses of nature, welling out from the bosom as
from a perennial spring, or stamped upon the senses by the
hand of their Maker. The power of the imagination in them
is the representative power of all nature. It has its centre
in the human soul, and makes the circuit of the universe."

Nor will any but the veriest curmudgeon find fault
with a child of the Revolution for concluding his first

lecture on poetry in general with some remarks on "four of the principal works of poetry in the world — Homer, the Bible, Dante, and Ossian."

> "We turn the weeding-clips aside,
> And spare the symbol dear."

If Hazlitt loved Ossian, so did Goethe.

Selma, Sagar, and Malvina, all are forgotten; but as we still chatter about style, one quotation must be assigned to that subject : —

"Arbuthnot's style is distinguished from that of his contemporaries even by a greater degree of terseness and conciseness. He leaves out every superfluous word; is sparing of connecting particles and introductory phrases; uses always the simplest forms of construction; and is more a master of the idiomatic peculiarities and internal resources of the language than almost any other writer. There is a research in the choice of a plain, as well as of an ornamental or learned, style; and, in fact, a great deal more. Among common English words, there may be ten expressing the same thing with different degrees of force and propriety, and only one of them the very word we want, because it is the only one that answers exactly with the idea we have in our minds. Each word in familiar use has a set of associations and shades of meaning attached to it, and distinguished from each other by inveterate custom; and it is in having the whole of these at our command, and in knowing which to choose, as they are called for by the occasion, that the perfection of a pure conversational prose style consists."

In the last lecture of the first course Hazlitt boldly tackles "The Living Poets." The fact that a man was alive never seemed to Hazlitt any reason for not saying what you thought of him in print. Hazlitt's essays came to be almost as much dreaded as Pope's couplets. The living poets if they saw Hazlitt's prospectus must have felt uneasy. The poet Rogers is most uncivilly treated; his breakfasts count simply for nothing; he is "an elegant but feeble writer," and there is no fault to be found with the *Pleasures of Memory*, except "a want of taste and genius"; the thoughts are "obvious," the words "tinsel," and the verses are poetry "chiefly because no particle, line, or syllable reads like prose." The poet Campbell is unfairly treated, and declared to belong to the same "hot-pressed superfine-wove paper" school as the poet Rogers. "He is a timid poet; and when he launches a sentiment that you think will float him triumphantly for once to the bottom of the stanza, he stops short at the end of the first or second line, and stands shivering on the bank of beauty." This may be true; but Campbell's verses on *Hohenlinden* have more than "considerable spirit and animation," nor ought the *Battle of the Baltic* to have been forgotten. What, however, probably annoyed Campbell most was the accusation that in altering Blair's lines —

> " Its visits,
> Like those of angels, short and far between,"

into

> " Like angel's visits, few and far between,"

he had spoilt them. " ' Few ' and ' far between ' are the same thing." It was nastily put, and made an enemy for life.

Tom Moore gets off very easily, though they were to quarrel afterwards over " The Fudge Family." Hazlitt liked his sentimental vein of fluttering fancy "glittering in the sun," and said he ought never to have written "Lalla Rookh" for three thousand guineas, which is a hard saying. Had he written it for nothing, one might have wondered.

Had Byron not wavered in his allegiance to Napoleon, he would have been a greater favourite with Hazlitt than he was; for they were both children of the Revolution, akin to Ossian and to Werther and the rest of that company of winds which, though

> "Upgathered now like sleeping flowers,"

once blew "great guns." They quarrelled, as relations sometimes will, over an inheritance. But Hazlitt is Byronic enough in his description of the poet to satisfy the most fancy-inflamed mantua-maker that ever in her garret by a spluttering farthing-dip pored over the *Corsair* : —

> " His brow collects the scattered gloom, his eye flashes livid fire that withers and consumes. But still we watch the progress of the scathing bolt with interest, and mark the ruin it leaves behind with awe. . . . He chooses elements and agents congenial to his mind — the dark and glittering ocean, the frail bark hurrying before the storm, pirates and men that 'house on the wild sea with wild usages.' He gives the tumultuous eagerness of action and the fixed despair of thought. In vigour of style and force of conception he in one sense surpasses every writer of the present day."

Great indeed was Byron. Just as a mournful Scotch proprietor judges of the strength of a gale of wind by walking through his plantations after it has dropped, and "moaning the expense" of many a fallen tree, so it is only by reading the lives and letters of his astonished contemporaries and immediate

successors that you are able to form some estimate
of the force of Byron.

For Scott's poetry Hazlitt had a true affection,
though one destined to be swallowed up in his passion
for the Waverley novels.

He next raises his hat to salute Wordsworth, "the
most original poet now living"; he then read aloud
the whole of "Hartleap Well," which was hardly
treating his audience fairly; and when it was over,
he observed fiercely, "Those who do not feel the
beauty and the force of this may save themselves the
trouble of inquiring further"— an offer that was probably freely accepted.   This civility was suspicious.
"I knew Jock Campbell meant to hang him from the
first," said a barrister present at Palmer's trial for
murder at Stafford, "he was so confoundedly polite to
the prisoner."   Hazlitt, after these preliminaries, proceeded to hang, not Wordsworth indeed, but his theory
of poetry.   "Wordsworth does not like even to share
his reputation with his *subject*, for he would have it *all*
to proceed from his own power and originality of
mind."   Hence that affection for idiot boys and mad
mothers —

> "Now heaven has placed it high 'mid human joys
> To talk with elf-lock girls and ragged boys" (*Landor*),

which so irritated many of Wordsworth's contemporaries.   "He tolerates only what he himself creates;" and then follows a vehement passage uplifted
from one of his political articles subsequently reprinted in the *Political Essays*.   Hazlitt was a Conser-
vative in poetry, nor was he ever a true revolutionary
in politics.

The lecture on "Living Poets," the last of the first series, concludes thus : —

"Coleridge's *Conciones ad Populum*, Watchman, etc., are dreary trash. Of his *Friend* I have spoken the truth elsewhere. But I may say of him here, that he is the only person I ever knew who answered to the idea of a man of genius. He is the only person from whom I ever learned anything. There is only one thing he could learn from me in return, but *that* he has not. He was the first poet I ever knew. His genius at that time had angelic wings, and fed on manna. He talked on for ever ; and you wished him to talk on for ever. His thoughts did not seem to come with labour and effort ; but as if borne on the gusts of genius, and as if the wings of his imagination lifted him from off his feet. His voice rolled on the ear like the pealing organ, and its sound alone was the music of thought. His mind was clothed with wings ; and, raised on them, he lifted philosophy to heaven. In his descriptions you then saw the progress of human happiness and liberty in bright and never-ending succession, like the steps of Jacob's ladder, with airy shapes ascending and descending, and with the voice of God at the top of the ladder. And shall I, who heard him then, listen to him now ? Not I ! That spell is broke ; that time is gone for ever ; that voice is heard no more ; but still the recollection comes rushing by with thoughts of long-past years, and rings in my ears with never-dying sound.

> ' What though the radiance which was once so bright
> Be now for ever vanish'd from my sight,
> Though nothing can bring back the hour
> Of glory in the grass, of splendour in the flow'r ;
>   I do not grieve, but rather find
>   Strength in what remains behind ;
>   In the primal sympathy,
>   Which having been, must ever be ;
>   In the soothing thoughts that spring
>   Out of human suffering ;
> In years that bring the philosophic mind ! '

"I have thus gone through the task I intended, and have come at last to the level ground.   I have felt my subject gradually sinking from under me as I advanced, and have been afraid of ending in nothing.   The interest has unavoidably decreased at almost every successive step of the progress, like a play that has its catastrophe in the first or second act. This, however, I could not help.   I have done as well as I could."

CHAPTER VIII

QUARRELS, ESSAYS, DELUSIONS, AND PICTURE GALLERIES

GIFFORD, " with his sword undrawn," if his weapon of offence is entitled to so honourable a noun, was always lying in wait for a new book by Hazlitt; and on the appearance of the *Lectures on the English Poets*, the editor of the *Quarterly Review* hastened to inform the respectable reading public that the lectures were "predatory incursions on truth and common-sense," threw "no gleam of light" upon their subject, "left no trace upon the mind of the reader," being indeed nothing but "an incoherent jumble of grand words." Hazlitt was declared, like Hannibal, to have bound himself by an oath, not against Rome, but against "accurate reasoning, just observation, and precise, or even intelligent, language." [1]

All contemporary criticism was not equally insensate. The *Quarterly Review*, with which Scott and Southey were proud to be connected though powerless to control,

[1] Gifford had been reading Dryden : —
> " As Hannibal did to the altars come,
> Sworn by his sire a mortal foe to Rome,
> So Shadwell swore, nor should his vow be vain,
> That he till death true dulness would maintain.
> And in his father's right and realm's defence
> Ne'er to have peace with wit nor truce with sense."
> — MACFLECKNOE.

was by far the worst offender. The *Scotsman* published,
in May and June 1818, two long reviews, friendly in
tone, indeed highly laudatory, and at the same time
discriminative. The reviewer observes with a force
every reader of Hazlitt must appreciate, "It is no
ordinary matter to peruse a book of Mr. Hazlitt's.
There is a certain *hurry of the spirit*, which never fails
to accompany the fine show of reason and taste under
which the mind is hardly at leisure to select beauties
or start objections." A hurry of the spirit is a fine
phrase, very applicable to Hazlitt, who bustles you
along. The *Scotsman*, naturally and properly, defends
a "brother Scot," the poet Campbell, against the
strictures of the Southron body.

After the publication of the third course a reviewer
in the *Edinburgh* discoursed with skill and taste concerning Hazlitt's critical gifts. Hazlitt, like Burke, is
so eloquent himself, that those who write about either
the one or the other generally try to be so too ; but
after the reviewer has got over the effort of telling us
how Hazlitt does not "dissect the form to show the
springs whence the blood flows," but makes us feel
"in the sparkling or softened eye, the wreathed smile
and the tender bloom," he becomes more useful, and it
would be hard to improve upon the following para-
graph : —

"Hazlitt has no lack of the deepest feelings, the profoundest sentiments of humanity, or the loftiest aspirations after
ideal good. But there are no great leading principles of taste
to give singleness to his aims, nor any central points in his
mind, around which his feelings may revolve and his imagi-
nations cluster. There is no sufficient distinction between his
intellectual and his imaginative faculties. He confounds the

truths of imagination with those of fact ; the processes of argument with those of feeling ; the immunities of intellect with those of virtue.   Hence the seeming inconsistency of many of his doctrines.   Hence the want of all continuity in his style.   Hence his failure in producing one single, harmonious, and lasting impression on the hearts of his hearers.   He never waits to consider whether a sentiment or an image is in place, so it be in itself striking.   That keen sense of pleasure in intellectual beauty, which is the best charm of his writings, is also his chief deluder.   He cannot resist a powerful image, an exquisite quotation, or a pregnant remark, however it may dissipate, or even subvert, the general feeling which his theme should inspire. . . .   He will never be contented to touch that most strange and curious instrument, the human heart, with a steady aim, but throws his hand rapidly over the chords, mingling strange discord with ‘most eloquent music.’ Instead of conducting us onward to a given object, he opens so many delicious prospects by the wayside, and suffers us to gaze at them so long, that we forget the end of our journey. He is perpetually dazzled among the sunbeams of his fancy, and plays with them in elegant fantasy, when he should point them to the spots where they might fall on truth and beauty, and render them visible by a clearer and lovelier radiance than had yet revealed them.” [1]

That this is searching criticism cannot be denied ; but Time, that old arbitrator, has, I think, corrected the reviewer in one respect.   Hazlitt’s *gusto* has served him in such excellent stead that, despite the absence of principles of taste and central points, and the encroachment of his intellectual upon his imaginative faculties, he has succeeded in making a permanent, though a mixed impression.   We know what his point of view was, and can flatter ourselves upon our ability, real or supposed, to outline his judgments upon the books, pictures, and plays of to-day.   For a critic to

[1] *Edinburgh Review*, vol. xxxiv.

be alive eighty years after publication of his criticisms is in itself a feat. Hazlitt can say with the
Abbé, *J'ai vécu.*

In 1819 Hazlitt was in no temper to put up with
the insolence of Gifford. The sale of the *Characters of
Shakespear's Plays* had ceased in consequence, as Hazlitt was perhaps right in thinking, of Gifford's attack;
his delightful contributions to the *Round Table* had
been stigmatised by the same authority as " loathsome
trash," " vulgar descriptions," " silly paradoxes," " flat
truisms," " misty sophistry," " broken English," and
now the *Lectures on the English Poets* were pronounced
" predatory incursions on truth and common-sense."
And all this by Gifford! Who was Gifford? " It is
time," says Hazlitt, " you were told what you are," and
down he sat to tell him. The result was —

A

LETTER

TO

WILLIAM GIFFORD, Esq.

FROM

WILLIAM HAZLITT, Esq.

" Fit pugil, et medicum urget "

LONDON

PRINTED FOR JOHN MILLER BURLINGTON ARCADE

PICCADILLY

1819

Price Three Shillings.

Hazlitt was never more philosophical than when in
a passion. He always gets a good thought-basis for his
hatreds; and he proceeded in this case to build up a
William Gifford, whom he afterwards criticises, with
that intimate acquaintance with the weak points of a
structure only the builder possesses. This gives freshness to what would otherwise be the dullest of dull
things — the abuse of a dead editor by a dead author.
Hazlitt, again like Burke, excelled in a quarrel, and
for the same reason : both were more than politicians,
more than authors, more than critics — they were, or
once had been, philosophers. Did any one quarrel, or
differ with, or abuse, either Burke or Hazlitt, straight-
way that person became in the eyes of both these
eminent men the personification of every evil influence
of the age, the abstract and brief chronicle of infamy.
Gifford, a spiteful creature enough, who had led a life
far harder than Hazlitt's, became, like the *Review* he
edited, "a receptacle for the scum and sediment of all
the prejudice, bigotry, ill-will, ignorance, and rancour
afloat in the kingdom." Everything that Hazlitt most
hated, dreaded, and despised, Gifford, so Hazlitt was
persuaded, loved and cherished, whilst whatever Hazlitt accounted worthy of all acceptation this miserable
Gifford spat upon and loathed.

"The character of Mr. Gifford's mind," so he wrote in his
essay on that person to be found in *The Spirit of the Age,*
"is an utter want of independence and magnanimity. He
cannot go alone, he must have crutches, a go-cart and tram-
mels, or he is timid, fretful, and helpless as a child. He
cannot conceive of anything different from what he finds it,
and hates those who pretend to a greater reach of intellect
or boldness of spirit than himself. He inclines, by a natural

and deliberate bias, to the traditional in laws and government; to the orthodox in religion; to the safe in opinion;
to the trite in imagination; to the technical in style; to
whatever implies a surrender of individual judgment into the
hands of authority, and a subjection of individual feeling to
mechanic rules. If he finds any one flying in the face of
these, or straggling from the beaten path, he thinks he has
them at a notable disadvantage, and falls foul of them without loss of time, partly to soothe his own sense of mortified
self-consequence, and as an edifying spectacle to his legitimate friends."

And again —

" He may call out with the fellow in the *Tempest,* I am
not Stephano, but a cramp. He would go back to the
standard of opinions, style, the faded ornaments, and insipid
formalities that came into fashion about forty years ago.
Flashes of thought, flights of fancy, idiomatic expressions, he
sets down among the signs of the times — the extraordinary
occurrences of the age we live in. They are marks of a restless and revolutionary spirit; they disturb the composure of
his mind and threaten the safety of the state."

One can still read this with pleasure, and give it
other names than Gifford's, which proves how necessary it is, would you keep your rage alive for a century,
to have a philosophic basis. If you cannot do this, the
wisest, as also the Christian thing to do, is to agree
with your adversary quickly. A specimen of the style
of the letter must be given; and as it was not all philosophy, I will select a fragment in which raillery
predominates. Gifford in his criticism of the *Round
Table* had pretended not to be able to tell the difference between Hazlitt and Leigh Hunt. On this,
Hazlitt —

"If, sir, your friend Mr. Hoppner, of whom, as you tell us, you discreetly said nothing while he was struggling with obscurity, lest it should be imputed to the partiality of friendship, but whom you praised and dedicated to as soon as he became popular, to show your disinterestedness and deference to public opinion, — if even this artist, whom you celebrate as a painter of flattering likenesses, had undertaken to unite in one piece the most striking features and characteristic expression of his and your common friends ; had improved your lurking archness of look into Mr. Murray's gentle, downcast obliquity of vision ; had joined Mr. Canning's drooping nose to Mr. Croker's aspiring chin, the clear complexion (the *splendida bilis*) of the one to the candid self-complacent aspect of the other ; had forced into the same preposterous medley the invincible *hauteur* and Satanic pride of Mr. Pitt's physiognomy, with the dormant meaning and admirable nonchalance of Lord Castlereagh's features, the manly sleekness of Charles Long, and the monumental outline of John Kemble — what mortal would have owned the likeness ! I too, sir, must claim the privilege of the *principium individuationis* for myself as well as my neighbours ; I will sit for no man's picture but my own, and not to you for that ; I am not desirous to play as many parts as Bottom ; and as to his ass's head, which you would put upon my shoulders, it will do for you to wear the next time you show yourself in Mr. Murray's shop, or for your friend Mr. Southey to take with him whenever he appears at Court."

In this spirited passage we see the portrait-painter. Hazlitt could not help admiring Castlereagh's looks.

The miscellaneous writers of to-day are sometimes blamed for their zeal in collecting their anonymous contributions to the papers and magazines, and making an honest book of them, fit for the shelves; but these gentlemen may, if they care to provoke comparisons, cite the examples of Hazlitt, Lamb, and De Quincey. Hazlitt was a hardened re-printer, and those who know all his books get familiar with passages which occur, word for word, in more even than two places. He repeats himself, using the same quotations, quite unblushingly, though the quotations indeed are seldom word for word the same, and still less frequently are they right.

Of all Hazlitt's books, the one most open to the dread charge of "Journalism" is the *Political Essays*, published in 1819, and dedicated in a manly strain to John Hunt:—

"The tried, steady, zealous, and conscientious advocate of the liberty of his country and the rights of mankind;—

"One of those few persons who are what they would be thought to be; sincere without offence, firm but temperate; uniting private worth to public principle; a friend in need, a patriot without an eye to himself; who never betrayed an individual or a cause he pretended to serve—in short, that rare character, a man of common sense and common honesty,

"This volume is respectfully and gratefully
"Inscribed by
"THE AUTHOR."

The preface excited the admiration of so good and sensible a judge as the author's son, who thought it the finest and most manly exposition of high political principle ever put forth; and were the book nothing but dedication and preface, it would be unexceptionable, but it is a closely printed octavo, numbering 439 pages, and of these 264 are devoted to reprinting letters to the newspapers, and articles therein, abusing Legitimacy, the war with France, the finances of Pitt, sham patriotism, Coleridge, and Southey, with force and wit, but after a furiously unfair and partisan fashion. The repetitions of this book become weari-

some; we are all by this time sick of *Wat Tyler.*
Southey (the more's the pity) has written himself
down, and there's an end of it.

The rest of the book is made up by again reprinting
" The Character of Pitt," and taking the characters of
Chatham, Fox, and Burke from *The Eloquence of the
British Senate*, and adding to these ten articles from
Leigh Hunt's short-lived *Yellow Dwarf.*

This publication did not turn away the wrath of
" William Gifford, Esq.," who, recognising, I suppose,
the value of a philosophic basis, now denounced Hazlitt in the *Quarterly* as " the slanderer of the human
race."

With this epithet hurled at, but hardly sticking to
him, I must approach some personal incidents in
Hazlitt's life.

It will not have escaped notice how completely we
have lost sight (save in the eloquent outburst reprinted
from the *Yellow Dwarf* at the end of the *Political
Essays*) of the elder Hazlitt. What, too, has become
of the mother whose birthplace in the far Fen country
her sentimental son had visited on foot, and of Peggy
the affectionate diarist. Hazlitt was once glad enough
of the shelter of his father's house in Wem. He was
a very bad correspondent, says his grandson, who con-
ceives it to be possible that since he moved from
home, he never traced a line to his father, mother, or
sister. " He never held," proceeds his biographer,
"any epistolary communication he could avoid with
his wife, son, or publishers, and friends of thirty
years' standing had not a scrap of his handwriting.
It was an idiosyncrasy." It was also a great pity, so
far at least as his father, mother, and sister were thus

neglected. With his wives and publishers I am not concerned.

Those who have to earn their livings by daily writing for the press may be excused if they are bad correspondents. Carlyles are rare, and, besides, Carlyle was never a journalist. The fact that Hazlitt found it easier to write splendid disquisitions about the essential grandeur of his father's character for money, than to drop the old man an occasional line of greeting for love, is regrettable, but quite consistent with the genuineness of his filial pride. A sentimentalist is usually better qualified to force *you* to honour his father and his mother than he is to keep the fifth commandment himself.

The elder Hazlitt had left Wem in 1814; and, after one or two changes, had settled down in retirement at Crediton, in an old house called Winswood, rental £24 a year. Here he died on the 16th of July 1820 in his eighty-fourth year, ministered to by his wife and daughter. His eloquent son was not by his father's side, nor was his address known at Winswood at the time. As a matter of fact, he was at Winterslow Hutt.

It was the duty of the diarist to tell her brother of their father's death. She did so as follows:—

"DEAR WILLIAM,—If we had known where to direct to you, we should not have sent Mary [1] to tell you of our father's death, but would have written to you directly; but neither your mother nor I were well enough to write at the time, and we thought Sarah might be on the road, and have been expecting her every night since. Your father's death was unexpected at last; for though we had been at one time

[1] John Hazlitt's second daughter.

doubtful of his living through the week, Mr. Nosworthy
thought him much better on Saturday morning. He died
on Sunday the 16th, about seven in the morning. To him
his death was a release from a state of suffering; he made
no complaint, nor did he give one groan, but went on talking of glory, honour, and immortality, and talking with me
to the last. His senses returned the last few hours; and
when he could not speak, he took my hand and put it into
mother's. He kept his bed but one day, and his appetite
was very good; but he had water on his chest, and that we
did not know for a long time, and we thought he might
have lived many months longer. My mother is very weak
and ill; it will be a long time before she recovers the distress and fatigue she has gone through. I am afraid I have
not written very clearly, as my head is so confused for want
of sleep. The habit of watching for so long a time prevents
my sleeping now. I hope I shall get better soon, and be
able to eat more than I do at present.

"My mother wishes to know if you intend to write anything in the *Repository*, giving some account of your father?
If you don't, somebody else will, and you can do it best.
Mr. Hinton was asking about it, and wished to know if he
could do anything for us in any way. The people here have
been very kind in doing and ordering everything for us that
we could not see about ourselves. Sarah intended to write
some in this letter, but she will not be back time enough.
We wish her to stay a week or two with us, now she is here.
We have got a bed to spare for you now whenever you like to
come. I hope you will write to us soon; my mother wishes
to hear from you, and know how you are. We all unite in
love to you. I have no more to say, but farewell, and may
God bless you. — I am your affectionate sister,

"P. HAZLITT.

"Crediton, July 28th (1820).
    "(Endorsed) W. HAZLITT, Esq.,
        "At the Hut, Winterslow, near Salisbury."

Hazlitt did not write the account for *The Repository*.
Mr. Hinton, who was a Unitarian divine, wrote it,

probably in a style more in unison with the general
tone of the obituary notices published in that paper
than anything from Hazlitt's pen would have proved.

We are told in the *Life* that in the manuscript of
the essay "On the Fear of Death," which appeared in
the second volume of *Table-Talk* (1822), there is the
following paraphrase of Miss Hazlitt's account of her
father's death, which does not appear in the printed
version: "I did not see my father after he was dead,
but I saw death shake him by the palsied hand and
stare him in the face. He made as good an end as
Falstaff, though different, as became him. After
repeating the name of his Redeemer often, he took my
mother's hand, and looking up, placed it in my sister's,
and expired. There was something graceful and
gracious in his nature, which showed itself in his
last act."

Hazlitt did well to strike this passage out. It is no
improvement on the original.

Hazlitt was not, as we have already seen, in sympathy with the new school of poetry, whether illustrated by the intense self-consciousness of Wordsworth
or the mystical fanaticism of Shelley. He was hard
to please ; and in an essay on "Paradox and Commonplace," which first appeared in the first volume of
Table-Talk (1821), he proceeded to philosophise about
the author of *Prometheus Unbound* in the following
strain : —

"The author of the *Prometheus Unbound* (to take an
individual instance of the last character) has a fire in his
eye, a fever in his blood, a maggot in his brain, a hectic
flutter in his speech, which mark out the philosophic fanatic.
He is sanguine-complexioned and shrill-voiced. As is often

observable in the case of religious enthusiasts, there is a slenderness of constitutional *stamina*, which renders the flesh no match for the spirit. His bending, flexible form appears to take no strong hold of things, does not grapple with the world about him, but slides from it like a river —

> ' And in its liquid texture mortal wound
> Receives no more than can the fluid air.'

The shock of accident, the weight of authority, make no impression on his opinions, which retire like a feather, or rise from the encounter unhurt, through their own buoyancy. He is clogged by no dull system of realities, no earth-bound feelings, no rooted prejudices, by nothing that belongs to the mighty trunk and hard husk of nature and habit, but is drawn up by irresistible levity to the regions of mere speculation and fancy, to the sphere of air and fire, where his delighted spirit floats in ' seas of pearl and clouds of amber.' There is no *caput mortuum* of wornout, threadbare experience to serve as ballast to his mind; it is all volatile intellectual salt of tartar, that refuses to combine its evanescent, inflammable essence with anything solid or anything lasting. Bubbles are to him the only realities — touch them, and they vanish. Curiosity is the only proper category of his mind; and though a man in knowledge, he is a child in feeling. Hence he puts everything into a metaphysical crucible to judge of it himself and exhibit it to others as a subject of interesting experiment, without first making it over to the ordeal of his common-sense or trying it on his heart. This faculty of speculating at random on all questions may, in its overgrown and uninformed state, do much mischief without intending it, like an overgrown child with the power of a man. Mr. Shelley has been accused of vanity — I think he is chargeable with extreme levity, but this levity is so great that I do not believe he is sensible of its consequences. He strives to overturn all established creeds and systems ; but this is in him an effect of constitution. He runs before the most extravagant opinions, but this is because he is held back by none of the merely me-

chanical checks of sympathy and habit. He tampers with
all sorts of obnoxious subjects, but it is less because he is
gratified with the rankness of the taint than captivated with
the intellectual phosphoric light they emit. It would seem
that he wished not so much to convince or inform as to shock
the public by the tenor of his productions, but I suspect he
is more intent upon startling himself with his electrical
experiments in morals and philosophy; and though they
may scorch other people, they are to him harmless amuse-
ments, the coruscations of an aurora borealis, that 'play
round the head, but do not reach the heart.' Still I could
wish that he would put a stop to the incessant, alarming
whirl of his voltaic battery. With his zeal, his talent, and
his fancy, he would do more good and less harm, if he were
to give up his wilder theories, and if he took less pleasure in
feeling his heart flutter in unison with the panicstruck
apprehensions of his readers."

This sermon greatly put out Leigh Hunt, who was
for ever fluttering in butterfly fashion round some
flower of the forest, and he wrote some angry letters
to Hazlitt protesting against the "cutting up" of a
brother reformer. Hazlitt's reply is printed for the
first time in the *Memoirs;* and being, as it is, full of
character, must be given at length : —

                              "Saturday night (April 21, 1821).

"MY DEAR HUNT, — I have no quarrel with you, nor can
I have. You are one of those people that I like, do what
they will ; there are others that I do not like, do what they
may. I have always spoken well of you to friend or foe, viz.
I have said you were one of the pleasantest and cleverest
persons I ever knew, but that you teased any one you had to
deal with out of their lives. I am fond of a theory, as you
know ; but I will give up even that to a friend if he shows
that he has any regard to my personal feelings. You provoke
me to think hard things of you, and then you wonder that I

hitch them into an essay, as if that made any difference. I pique myself on doing what I can for others; but I cannot say that I have found any suitable returns for this, and hence perhaps my outrageousness of stomach ! For instance, I praised you in the *Edinburgh Review;* and when in a case of life and death I tried to lecture, you refused to go near the place, and gave this as a reason, saying it would seem a collusion if you said anything in my favour after what I had said of you. 2. I got Reynolds to write in the *Edinburgh Review* at a time when I had a great reluctance to ask any favour of Jeffrey, and from that time I never set eyes on him for a year and a half after. 3. I wrote a book in defence of Godwin some years ago, one-half of which he has since stolen without acknowledgment, without even mentioning my name, and yet he comes to me to review the very work, and I write to Jeffrey to ask his consent, thinking myself, which you do not, the most magnanimous person in the world in the defence of a cause. 4. I have taken all opportunities of praising Lamb, and I never got a good word from him in return, big or little, till the other day. He seemed struck all of a heap if I ever hinted at the possibility of his giving me a lift at any time. 5. It was but the other day that two friends did all they could to intercept an article about me from appearing in the *E. R.*, saying ‘ it would be too late,’ ‘ that the editor had been sounded at a distance, and was averse,’ with twenty other excuses ; and at last I was obliged to send it myself, *graciously* and by main force, as it were, when it appeared just in time to save me from drowning. Coulson had been backwards and forwards between my house and Bentham’s for between three or four years; and when the latter philosophically put an execution in my house, the plea was that he had never heard of my name ; and when I theorised on this the other day as bad policy, and *felo de se* on the part of the Radicals, your nephew [1] and that set said, ‘ Oh, it was an understood thing — the execution, you know ! ’ My God, it is enough to drive one mad. I have not a soul to stand by me, and yet I am to give up my only resource and revenge, a theory — I won’t do it, that’s flat.

[1] Mr. Henry Leigh Hunt, of the firm of Hunt and Clarke.

Montagu[1] is, I fancy, cut at my putting him among people
with one idea, and yet when the Blackwoods (together with
your) shirking out of that business put me nearly under-
ground, he took every opportunity to discourage me; and one
evening, when I talked of going there, I was given to understand that there was 'a party expected.' Yet after this I am
not to look at him a little *in abstracto*. This is what has
soured me, and made me sick of friendship and acquaintance-
ship. When did I speak ill of your brother John? He never
played me any tricks. I was in a cursed ill humour with you
for two or three things when I wrote the article you find fault
with (I grant not without reason). If I had complained to
you, you would only have laughed; you would have played
me the very same tricks the very next time; you would not
have cared one farthing about annoying me; and yet you complain that I draw a logical conclusion from all this, and publish it to the world without your name. As to Shelley, I do
not hold myself responsible to him. You say I want *imagination*. If you mean invention or fancy, I say so too; but
if you mean a disposition to sympathise with the claims or
merits of others, I deny it. I have been too much disposed
to waive my own pretensions in deference to those of others.
I am tired with playing at rackets all day, and you will be
tired with this epistle. It has little to do with you; for I
see no use in raising up a parcel of small, old grievances.
But I think the general ground of defence is good.
                                                      "W. H.

"I have given Hogg's papers to Baldwin, and wish you
would write a character of me for the next number. I want
to know why everybody has such a dislike to me."

Hazlitt may have been unreasonable in finding fault
with Lamb, whose opportunities of praising Hazlitt
cannot have been many, but what he says as to his
own conduct in praising Lamb whenever he got a

---

[1] Mr. Basil Montagu.

chance is only the truth. But when Southey thought
fit to reproach Lamb in public for his friendship (then,
as it happened, suspended) with Hazlitt, nobly indeed
did Elia take the field and rout the foe.

Hazlitt's " I want to know why everybody has such a
dislike to me " is pathetic. He could not understand it.

The reference to " playing rackets all day " justifies
a word or two about Hazlitt's fondness for the game,
which he played with a fierce eagerness, sometimes
lying awake a whole night trying to score out the last
ball of an interesting game in a particular corner of the
court which he had missed from nervousness. He
philosophises even about rackets, remarking that
though it is very like any other game, very much a
thing of skill and practice, it is also a thing of opinion,
" subject to all the skiey influences." " If you think
you can win, you can win. Faith is necessary for
victory," and so on down half a page.[1]

He was also very fond of fives, both of playing and
seeing it played. His short life of John Cavanagh is
one of Hazlitt's finest performances. One could wish
that *Boxiana* was in the least like it, and that Hazlitt
had written the *History of Fisticuffs* instead of a *Life
of Napoleon.*

" Died at his house in Burbage Street, St. Giles's, John
Cavanagh, the famous hand fives-player. When a person
dies who does any one thing better than any one else in the
world, which so many others are trying to do well, it leaves a
gap in society. It is not likely that any one will now see the
game of fives played in its perfection for many years to come,

---

[1] Haydon once met Hazlitt returning from the Fives-court with
his shirt in his pocket. He had been playing rackets with such
energy that his shirt was like a wet rag. — *Hazlitt Memoirs*, ii. 35.

for Cavanagh is dead, and has not left his peer behind him.
It may be said that there are things of more importance than
striking a ball against a wall. There are things indeed which
make more noise and do as little good, such as making war
and peace, making speeches and answering them, making
verses and blotting them, making money and throwing it
away. But the game of fives is what no one despises who has
ever played at it. . . . As it was said of a great orator that
he never was at a loss for a word, and for the properest word,
so Cavanagh always could tell the degree of force necessary
to be given to a ball, and the precise direction in which it
should be sent. He did his work with the greatest ease ;
never took more pains than was necessary ; and while others
were fagging themselves to death, was as cool and collected as
if he had just entered the court. His style of play was as
remarkable as his power of execution. He had no affectation,
no trifling. He did not throw away the game to show off an
attitude or try an experiment. He was a fine, sensible,
manly player, who did what he could, but that was more than
any one else could even affect to do. His blows were not
undecided and ineffectual, lumbering like Mr. Wordsworth's
epic poetry, nor wavering like Mr. Coleridge's lyric prose, nor
short of the mark like Mr. Brougham's speeches, nor wide of
it like Mr. Canning's wit, nor foul like the *Quarterly*, not *let*
balls like the *Edinburgh Review.* Cobbett and Junius together would have made a Cavanagh. He was the best *up-
hill* player in the world ; even when his adversary was
fourteen, he would play on the same or better ; and as he
never flung away the game through carelessness and conceit,
he never gave it up through laziness or want of heart. The
only peculiarity of his play was that he never *volleyed*, but let
the balls hop ; but if they rose an inch from the ground, he
never missed having them. There was not only nobody equal,
but nobody second to him. It is supposed that he could give
any other player half the game, or beat him with his left
hand. His service was tremendous. He once played Wood-
ward and Meredith together (two of the best players in
England) in the Fives-court, St. Martin's Street, and made
seven-and-twenty aces following by services alone — a thing

unheard of. He another time played Peru, who was considered a first-rate fives-player, a match of the best out of
five games ; and in the three first games, which of course decided
the match, Peru got only one ace. Cavanagh was an Irishman
by birth, and a house-painter by profession. . . . He used
frequently to play matches at Copenhagen House for wagers
and dinners. The wall against which they play is the same
that supports the kitchen chimney ; and when the wall
resounded louder than usual, the cooks exclaimed, ' Those are
the Irishman's balls,' and the joints trembled on the spit !
Goldsmith consoled himself that there were places where he too
was admired ; and Cavanagh was the admiration of all the
fives-courts where he ever played. . . . Mr. Powell, when
he played matches in the Court in St. Martin's Street, used
to fill his gallery at half-a-crown a head with amateurs and
admirers of talent in whatever department it is shown. He
could not have shown himself in any ground in England but
he would have been immediately surrounded with inquisitive
gazers, trying to find out in what part of his frame his un-
rivalled skill lay, as politicians wonder to see the balance of
Europe suspended in Lord Castlereagh's face, and admire the
trophies of the British Navy lurking under Mr. Croker's
hanging brow. Now Cavanagh was as good looking a man as
the Noble Lord, and much better looking than the Right
Hon. Secretary. He had a clear, open countenance, and did
not look sideways or down. He was a young fellow of sense,
humour, and courage. He once had a quarrel with a water-
man at Hungerford stairs, and, they say, served him out in
great style. In a word, there are hundreds at this day who
cannot mention his name without admiration as the best
fives-player that perhaps ever lived (the greatest excellence of
which they have any notion), and the noisy shout of the ring
happily stood him in stead of the unheard voice of posterity !
The only person who seems to have excelled as much in another way as Cavanagh did in his was the late John Davies,
the racket-player. It was remarked of him that he did not
seem to follow the ball, but the ball seemed to follow him.
Give him a foot of wall, and he was sure to make the ball.
The four best racket-players of that day were Jack Spines,

Jem Harding, Armitage, and Church.   Davies could give any
one of these two hands a time, that is, half the game, and each
of these, at their best, could give the best player now in
London the same odds.   Such are the gradations in all exer-
tions of human skill and art.   He once played four capital
players together and beat them.   He was also a first-rate
tennis-player, and an excellent fives-player.   In the Fleet or
King's Bench he would have stood against Powell, who was
reckoned the best open-ground player of his time.   This last-
mentioned player is at present the keeper of the Fives-court,
and we might recommend to him for a motto over his door,
'Who enters here, forgets himself, his country, and his
friends.'   And the best of it is, that by the calculation of the
odds, none of the three are worth remembering !   Cavanagh
died from the bursting of a blood-vessel, which prevented him
from playing for the last two or three years.   This, he was
often heard to say, he thought hard upon him.   He was fast
recovering, however, when he was suddenly carried off, to the
regret of all who knew him.   As Mr. Peel made it a qualification of the present Speaker, Mr. Manners Sutton, that he was
an excellent moral character, so Jack Cavanagh was a zealous
Catholic, and could not be persuaded to eat meat on a Friday,
the day on which he died.   We have paid this willing tribute
to his memory —

> ' Let no rude hand deface it,
> And his forlorn Hic Jacet.' " [1]

If any reader thinks this too long a quotation about
a fives-player, I will silence him with another, a very
short one, from the essay *On the Ignorance of the
Learned* —

"It is better to be able neither to read nor write than to
be able to do nothing else."

The famous "Fight" appeared in 1822 in the *New
Monthly Magazine*.   From it I will not quote.   As

[1] 'The Indian Jugglers.' — *Table-Talk*.

Oxford was once declared to be, by an enthusiast, after dinner, "it is a perfect whole," and must not be curtailed, as I was compelled to curtail Cavanagh. It is full of poetry, life, and motion; Shakespeare, Hogarth, and Nature. The description of the actual fight is not long, which perhaps is as well, for it is vivid. A phrase Tennyson has made famous occurs in it, for Hazlitt speaks of Bill Neate making "red ruin" of Tom Hickman's cheek.

Table-Talk has already been mentioned more than once; but it should be here formally recorded that it was another collection of miscellaneous essays, only a few of which (less than half a dozen) had been printed before. Mr. Henry Colburn, a pushing, advertising publisher, alleged to have royal blood in his veins, brought it out in two volumes (1821 and 1822).

These two volumes standing alone contain enough to establish Hazlitt's reputation as one of the greatest miscellaneous writers that ever lived. The very titles of the papers make you a-hungered to read them. The essays "On Going a Journey," "On the Fear of Death," "On Patronage and Puffing," "The Indian Jugglers," "On a Landscape by Nicolas Poussin," are compositions of which no sensible man, who happens to be fond of reading (and many sensible men are not), can ever grow tired. Of the miscellaneous writer one does not demand settled principles of taste or deep searching criticism; it is enough if he at once arrests, and throughout maintains our attention; if he hurries our sluggish spirit up and down animated pages; if he is never vapid, or humdrum, or foolish, or blatant, or self-satisfied; if he forces us to forget ourselves; and by renewing our delight in books, poetry, plays,

pictures, and in the humours and emotions of life,
makes us feel that it was really worth our while not
only to have learned to read, but to have gone on reading ever since.

Gifford was content on the appearance of *Table-Talk*
to add to the title of " Slanderer of the Human Race "
that of " Slang Whanger," meaning thereby, he was
good enough to explain, " a gabbler who employs
slang to amuse the rabble." But any deficiency of
abuse noticeable in the style of the *Quarterly* was
amply atoned for by Professor Wilson's merry men in
Blackwood, who declared that the Table-Talker was
not a man, but an ulcer; that his two volumes were
one gaping sore of wounded feeling and vanity; nor
were they content with a single reference to Hazlitt,
who henceforth became one of the favourite marks of
their goat-footed merriment.

Hazlitt, if Mr. Patmore is to be believed, was driven
almost mad by these Yahoos; and it may be that the
irregularities and coarse excesses of this period of his
life may be in part attributed to an unhinging of the
mind occasioned by repeated personal abuse. It is a
pity Hazlitt was not a fighting man; he might then
have called Christopher North out; and if he had by
chance deposited several large slugs in the Professor's
acromion process, "thereby endangering his life and
lacerating the clavicle of his right shoulder," only
good would have been done. He did threaten legal
proceedings with one good result — Mr. John Murray
refused any longer to act for " Maga " in London.

The establishment in 1820 of the *London Magazine*,
sometimes called *Baldwin's*, and sometimes *Taylor's
Magazine*, should be mentioned in a Life of Hazlitt,

who for a few years contributed to it both dramatic and fine art criticisms, as well as numerous miscellaneous essays, which were all afterwards reprinted in the *Plain Speaker* (1826) or elsewhere, with one notable exception — an article in the October number for 1820 on the "Present State of Parliamentary Eloquence."

In this essay Hazlitt passes in review Mackintosh, Brougham, Whitbread, Tierney, Ponsonby, Plunkett, Castlereagh, Wilberforce, Canning, and other speakers in an admirable and for the most part convincing fashion, though I find it hard to bear the references to Sir Samuel Romilly. "I did not much like Romilly's significant oracular way of laying down the law in the House, his self-important assumptions of second-hand truths, and his impatience of contradiction, as if he gave his time there for nothing." How well do I know the style! but that it should be Romilly's! I cannot, I must not, believe it.

The early numbers of the *London Magazine* contain as their proud possessions the first essays of "Elia." "The South Sea House" is in the August number for 1820, "Oxford in the Vacation" follows in October, and "Christ's Hospital Five and Thirty Years Ago" is in the November number, which also contained a savage onslaught upon *Blackwood*, to be succeeded in the December number by an even more furious attack upon the same shameless offender. These *Blackwood* articles impart a melancholy to the early volumes of the *London Magazine* which even "Elia" cannot dispel; for they still seem red with the blood of John Scott, the first editor, who was, so it is believed, the writer of the articles in question.

Whether John Scott in abusing *Blackwood* as he did
in his new magazine was chiefly animated by holy
wrath, and a desire to avenge the undoubted wrongs
of Hazlitt and Leigh Hunt, and of a greater than
either, or by that first and last infirmity of the journalist's mind, to attract attention to his new venture,
cannot be told.   Mr. Lockhart, whose name was freely
mentioned in the December article, considered himself aggrieved, bade farewell to his young wife about
to lie in of her first child — Hugh Littlejohn, known
to us all — and came to London to demand and receive
satisfaction, which Scott would not give unless Lockhart first repudiated any connection, either as editor,
or financially, with the management of *Blackwood*.
Lockhart, who acted throughout under the advice of
his old Balliol friend Mr. J. H. Christie, a man of
the nicest honour, who viewed with no little disap-
proval Lockhart's unhappy connection with the Edinburgh press, refused to give Scott more than an
assurance that he was not editor of *Blackwood*.   There
was therefore a deadlock; but honour being a nice
matter resting in report, both Lockhart and Scott
took to printing "Statements" for circulation among
friends, and Lockhart in his first statement, an early
copy of which he sent to his adversary with the significant message that the sender would remain in London for twenty-four hours, denied that he was editor
of *Blackwood*, but said nothing as to deriving any
benefit from the management of the magazine.   A few
hours after sending Scott this statement, Lockhart and
Christie were advised by Dr. Stoddart (Hazlitt's
brother-in-law, then in charge of a paper called *The
New Times*, of so limited a circulation as to prompt

Hazlitt, who hated Stoddart, to say that any one who really wished to keep a secret could not do better than confide it to the columns of his relative's newspaper) that Lockhart's case would be improved by the additional statement that he had never derived any pecuniary benefit from the management of *Blackwood*. This addition was made, and the statement thus amended circulated. When Scott saw the amended statement, which he did not do until Lockhart had left London, he at once pounced upon the new matter, and in one of his statements [1] said that Lockhart had told his friends something he had not told Scott, but which if he had been told would have made a meeting possible. This was a nasty thrust, and made an immediate answer from Christie, Lockhart being away, an absolute necessity. Mr. Christie therefore told in print how the addition came to be made on the advice of Stoddart; and added a few sarcastic words to the effect that if after his explanation Scott had any friends who were not satisfied, he was welcome to the whole weight of their good opinion. Thereupon Scott, who had not seemed over-eager to fight Lockhart, fell upon Christie and demanded that he should say in public that he meant nothing disrespectful to Scott, and on Christie's refusal sent him a challenge.

The story so far is a Comedy of Errors; it was now to become a Tragedy. Scott's "friends" were Mr. Patmore (the father of the poet) and Mr. Horatio Smith, two hopelessly incompetent persons. Mr. Christie's friend was Mr. Traill, the father of Mr. H. D. Traill. Mr. Patmore alone was with Scott at

---

[1] Scott's statements may be read in the *London Magazine* for February 1821, and Lockhart's in Mr. Lang's *Life*.

Chalk Farm on the 16th of February 1821. Christie fired in the air, Scott fired and missed. The matter ought then to have been ended by Mr. Patmore declaring himself satisfied; but second shots were allowed to be interchanged, and this time Scott fell mortally wounded. He died on the 27th of the month, leaving a widow and two children.

Mr. Lang, who recounts the whole affair with candour and feeling in his *Life of Lockhart*, successfully vindicates Lockhart from any blame in this unfortunate and bungled business; and as for Mr. Christie, if he had been a Generalissimo of Spain, instead of a Conveyancer of Lincoln's Inn, he could not have behaved better.

The poet Campbell, who never forgot the charge of plagiarising Blair's *Angels' Visits*, used to go about saying that Hazlitt had egged Scott on to fight by remarking that, of course, he (Hazlitt) was not a fighting man; but if he had been, why then, etc., etc. There is no need to believe this. Scott and Hazlitt were not intimate friends, and no traces remain of the latter having been personally mixed up in the affair either in its early stages with Lockhart or at the end with Christie.

It is impossible in a Life of Hazlitt entirely to overlook the brutalities of the early numbers of *Blackwood's Magazine*, but they are now far off, if not forgotten, things; and even as I write, there comes to hand from the firm of William Blackwood & Sons, in their series of English Classics, an excellently made selection (with a portrait without pimples) from Hazlitt's *Lectures and Essays on Poetry and Poets*. The editor, Mr. D. Nichol Smith, whilst sarcastically observing that Gifford's

treatment of Hazlitt in the *Quarterly* forms an interesting chapter in the history of reviewing, maintains a
judicious silence about any other reviews or reviewers.
The less said the better. Let us keep a guard upon
our own tongues and pens. Biographers must, however, be allowed a reasonable licence. Hazlitt was
unhappily, unlike Sir Joshua Reynolds, a vulnerable
man ; and if he was hit hard and below the belt, he
hit back again as hard as he could, and sometimes I
am afraid below the belt.[1]

Two matters, however, in which Hazlitt was undeniably mixed up now present themselves for treatment — the divorce in Scotland, and the affair with
Miss Walker, which latter unpleasant delusion has to
be mentioned only because it is buried or embalmed
in a book of Hazlitt's it is impossible to ignore, though
disagreeable to read — the *Liber Amoris* (1823).

Of the two incidents, the Scotch divorce, involving
as it does a few legal points, is (by comparison) almost
cheerful.

Hazlitt's relations with his wife were, what we have
seen, uncomfortable ; they did not hate each other,
and they were both attached to the boy, but they

---

[1] It is impossible to offer any apology for some of Hazlitt's
articles in the *Examiner* and *Edinburgh Review* about Coleridge.
Whether the latter took a worthy revenge in concocting or adapt-
ing the following epitaph or epigram on hearing of Hazlitt's death,
I leave for the reader's consideration : —

> " Under this stone does William Hazlitt lie
> Who valued nought }
> *Thankless of all* } that God or man could give.
> He lived like one who never thought to die,
> He died like one who dared not hope to live."

As a criticism of Hazlitt it is singularly *mal à propos.*

were quite willing to part company. Hazlitt's habits
as a husband had become bad; and but for an amazing
bluntness of feeling on his wife's part, would have
been unendurable. He also made complaints about
her. In 1819 they had given up joint housekeeping
in York Street, and were living apart. In August
1820 Hazlitt saw Miss Walker, and became infatuated.
The married pair were minded to be quit of the yoke.
How was it to be done?

In England until 1857 there was no Divorce Court,
such as is now the pride of the land, but the Spiritual
Court would on proof of certain matrimonial offences
decree a separation *a mensa et thoro ;* and then if it
was the husband who had obtained the decree, he could,
if rolling in money, and after recovering damages
in a civil action, promote the passage through both
Houses of Parliament of a Bill which, if it passed, put
an end altogether to the marriage formerly subsisting
between him and his wife, and left both at liberty to
marry again. It was, I believe, the practice of the
Bishops in the House of Lords when a Divorce Bill
was in Committee to depute one of their number to
move an amendment forbidding either the husband
or wife to marry again during the lifetime of the
other, and this amendment was usually allowed to
be carried, on the honourable understanding that at
a later stage the original clause should be restored —
as it always was.

England was clearly of no use in Hazlitt's case.
Some kind friend directed his attention to Scotland.
There the law was very different. In Scotland in
1823, as now, either spouse could on proof of the unfaithfulness of the other obtain in the proper Court

a decree annulling the marriage and restoring to both
parties the freedom to marry again. This sounds
fair, and may be so; but the result is, that whenever
the parties to a matrimonial contract or relationship
in Scotland are minded to be rid of the obligation,
and the husband has no incurable objection to formal
proof being tendered of a single act of unfaithfulness
on his part, there is an end of the marriage.

Hazlitt had no delicacy of this disabling kind, and
to Scotland accordingly the parties went, not to be
married, but to be divorced.[1]   The husband stopped,
or was stopped, perhaps, by want of money, at Stamford, where he could find, so he tells us, no more
agreeable way of passing the time than by writing
in a tradesman's book — a butterman's, I think — the
first part of the *Liber Amoris.* Mrs. Hazlitt followed
by sea, landing at Leith one Sunday morning in April
1822; and in Edinburgh she chiefly remained till the
18th of July, when her marriage being annulled, at
all events, by Scotch law, she returned to London on
the smack *Favourite* a free woman. Her husband was
in Edinburgh or the neighbourhood during the same
period, and they occasionally met, had a cup of tea
together, and abused with all the ingratitude of suitors
"the law's delay." Hazlitt managed to turn an honest
and much-needed penny by lecturing at Glasgow at
the Andersonian Institute on Milton and Shakespeare,

---

[1] In 1823 it was settled law in Scotland that if the defender in an
action for divorce had been resident for *forty* days within Scotland,
he was amenable to the jurisdiction of the Court. This is no longer
good Scotch law, and was never recognised as law at all in England.
Hazlitt's second marriage in England was bigamous. (See *R.* v.
Lolley, Russell and Ryan, 237. This case was commented upon by
Brougham in the *Edinburgh Review*, vol. xlvii. p. 112.)

Thomson and Burns; and chancing to hear Dr.
Chalmers preach, he made excellent copy out of the
occasion for publication in that terrible paper the
Liberal, which in Wordsworth's inflamed fancy "was
to be directed against everything in religion, in
morals, and probably in Government and literature,
which our forefathers have been accustomed to reverence." Poor Mrs. Hazlitt had no such gifts, and was
sometimes left with only four shillings and sixpence
in her pocket, but none the less she somehow managed
pendente lite to enjoy herself not a little, whiling away
the time between repeated adjournments by a trip
through the Trossachs, roaming through the fair
domains of Dalmeny, and even taking shipping to
Ireland and visiting both Dublin and Belfast.

The whole scheme was nearly wrecked and Hazlitt
driven distracted by this good woman's scruples. She
was confronted with the oath *de calumnia*, which, as
it required her to swear on her knees with her right
hand on the Gospels that there had been no concert
between her and her husband in order to obtain a
divorce, might well occasion her some uneasiness, for
no other business had brought them both to Edinburgh. In her distress, for she was not a dishonest
woman, she consulted a member of the Scottish Bar, [1]
who assured her that the oath was only meant to hit
cases where no real matrimonial offence had ever been
committed; and as in her case Hazlitt had committed
such offences both in London and in Edinburgh, she
might fairly take it, which accordingly she did.

Hazlitt, I need not say, put in no substantial defence

---

[1] Mr. Cranstoun, afterwards Lord Corehouse.

to his wife's plaint; formal proof was tendered of a matrimonial offence in Edinburgh, and the desired decree pronounced. The expenses were inconsiderable, £26, 10s. 9d.[1]

Mrs. Hazlitt's Journal kept in Scotland during this visit is published in a recent edition of the *Liber Amoris*, and is worth a cartload of such books. It is, in its naïveté and bluntness, a remarkable record of the most unsentimental journey ever taken — not but what Mrs. Hazlitt had, as the Journal shows, a fine eye for scenery, and could criticise the pictures in Dalkeith Palace with the eye of a connoisseur.

This collusive divorce, though separating the parties, in no way affected their friendliness of feeling. Mrs. Hazlitt frequently visited old Mrs. Hazlitt and Peggy, and never wrote or spoke otherwise than affectionately of "William," and they also occasionally met. Their son was happily able to entertain sincere affection for both his parents.

The other matter might be disposed of once for all in Hazlitt's own words, written the very same year that saw the publication of the *Liber Amoris* — he is citing acquaintances of his own who have been ruined with their eyes wide open by some whim or fancy, and he mentions one "who divorced his wife to marry a wench at a lodging-house, who refused to have him, and whose cruelty and charms are the torments of his

---

[1] My friend Mr. William Mitchell, S.S.C., of Edinburgh, has been kind enough to examine in the General Record Room in the Register House the process of Divorce in the Consistorial Court of *Stoddart* or *Hazlitt* v. *Hazlitt*, which, he tells me, verifies in all particulars Mrs. Hazlitt's narrative, whilst rendering no support to the scandalous version Hazlitt is reported to have given to Landor in Florence (see Landor's *Life*, vol. ii. p. 207).

own life and that of all his friends." This is very near
the truth, though as Hazlitt was not a Tudor monarch,
he could hardly have divorced his wife, even in Scotland, had she not been quite willing to be quit of him
on account of his infidelities.

The loves of the middle-aged are never agreeable
subject-matter for the pens of third parties.

"A fool at forty is a fool indeed,"

and this affair of Hazlitt's must be briefly handled.

The *Liber Amoris*, which has been written about in
glowing terms by a gentle lady, and pronounced " delightful " by a noble lord, is divided into three parts.
The first, written at Stamford in the circumstances
before stated, consists of conversations supposed to
have been held between the anonymous author and
the girl at the lodging-house. The second consists of
extracts from letters actually addressed to an unnamed
friend (Patmore), in which are unfolded the passion,
fury, and delusion of the writer, who declares the
persistency of his devotion in spite of much that might
well have killed it. The third part is made up of
three long letters to another unnamed friend (Mr.
Sheridan Knowles) narrating the conclusion of the
affair — the treachery, wantonness, and hypocrisy of
the girl who would have nothing to say to him, pre-
ferring the addresses of another lodger.

The facts upon which the book is supposed to rest
are now offensively familiar. Miss Walker was not a
servant girl properly so called, but a tailor's daughter
whose mother kept a lodging-house in Southampton
Buildings. The tailor had three daughters. The

eldest had married respectably, and she and her husband were known to Hazlitt; Sarah, the second daughter, is described by Procter as having a round small face, glassy eyes, a snake-like walk, and being very silent and demure, with a steady unmoving, uncomfortable gaze upon the person she was addressing, but Hazlitt gives a slightly more agreeable portrait in his *Table-Talk* where he writes : —

" The greatest hypocrite I ever knew was a little, demure, pretty, modest-looking girl with eyes timidly cast upon the ground and an air soft as enchantment. The only circumstance that could lead to a suspicion of her true character was a cold, sullen, watery, glazed look about the eyes, which she bent on vacancy, as if determined to avoid all explanation with yours. I might have spied in their glittering, motionless surface the rocks and quicksands that awaited one below."[1]

Of the genuineness of Hazlitt's infatuation there can be no doubt, although *Liber Amoris* itself is not a book of good faith. Procter's account of it would be amusing but for the subject-matter. " His (Hazlitt's) intellect was completely subdued by an insane passion. He was, for a time, unable to think or talk of anything else. He abandoned criticism and books as idle matters, and fatigued every person whom he met by expressions of her love, of her deceit, and of his own vehement disappointment. This was when he lived in Southampton Buildings, Holborn. Upon one occasion I know that he told the story of his attachment to five different persons in the same day, and at each time entered into minute details of his love story. ' I am a cursed fool,' said he to me. ' I saw J—— going

[1] Essay on the *Knowledge of Character.*

into Wills' Coffee House yesterday morning; he spoke
to me. I followed him into the house, and whilst he
lunched I told him the whole story. Then I wandered
into the Regent's Park, where I met one of M——'s
sons. I walked with him some time, and on his using
some civil expression, by Jove, sir, I told him the whole
story!' (Here he mentioned another instance which I
forget.) 'Well, sir' (he went on), 'I then went and
called on Haydon, but he was out. There was only
his man, Salmon, there; but, by Jove, I could not help
myself. It all came out — the whole cursed story.
Afterwards I went to look at some lodgings at Pimlico.
The landlady at one place, after some explanations as
to rent, etc., said to me very kindly, "I am afraid you
are not well, sir?" "No, ma'am," said I, "I am not
well," and on inquiring further, the devil take me if I
did not let out the whole story from beginning to end.'"[1]

Lord Houghton once wrote in the *Fortnightly Review*
"of the wondrous servant girl who drove Hazlitt mad
by the dignity that petrified her beauty and froze the
passion it inflamed."[2] "Wondrous" and "dignity"
are strange words to apply to the *Liber Amoris*; but
no doubt when he set about concocting the book, the
literary point Hazlitt wished to make was that, like the
madman in *Don Quixote* he is for ever quoting, "he
had worshipped a statue, hunted the wind, and cried
aloud in the desert." His literary failure to make out
any adequate image of a damsel in stone is to be accounted for by his having printed in the book too
much of his original letters to Patmore and Knowles.
He did not cut out enough, and what he left in spoiled

---

[1] Procter's *Autobiographical Fragments* (1873).
[2] *Fortnightly Review*, January 1881, 'Notes on *Endymion*.'

the romance without telling the truth. The letters, as actually written by Hazlitt to Patmore and Knowles, are now unhappily in print. How they came to be preserved is beyond guessing. Preserved however they were, and printed they have been. I will say no more about them than that they make the subject intolerable. If the statements made in them are true, the tailor's wife was a Doll Tearsheet, and her house and her daughter (her prudish tongue notwithstanding) what the house and daughter of Doll Tearsheet might be expected to be. On the other hand, it would be grossly unfair not to remember that neither tailor's wife nor daughter has ever been heard in her own defence; and that the girl, whose wisdom in refusing to marry Hazlitt cannot be disputed, subsequently made, as her sister before her had done, what is called a respectable marriage.

Anyhow, the whole sentimental structure of the *Liber Amoris* now sinks below the stage, and joins the realm of things unspeakable — " vile kitchen stuff," fit only for the midden.

Hazlitt got £100 for the *Liber Amoris*, which John Hunt published in 1823. It is easy to imagine the unholy joy of *Blackwood*, whose writers were not likely to overlook a casual reference it contains to Craigcrook, " where lives the prince of critics and the king of men." It was certainly hard upon Jeffrey to be dragged into such mire.

Two things may usefully be remembered. Hazlitt wrote some of his best essays during the duration of this madness — for example, nearly the whole of the second volume of *Table-Talk*, including the noble discourse " On the Fear of Death "; and in another

style, but equally triumphant, the famous "Fight."
Secondly, the filial language of Hazlitt's son: "For
some time previous to this my father had fallen into
an infatuation which he himself illustrated in glowing
and eloquent language in a regretted publication called
Liber Amoris. The subject is a painful one, and
admits of but one cheerful consolation — that my
father's name and character was but momentarily
dimmed by what indeed was but a momentary delusion."

"O Art, lovely Art, 'balm of hurt minds, chief
nourisher in life's feast, great Nature's second course,'
thee we invoke, and not in vain." In this somewhat
braggadocio mood do we find Hazlitt, in the December
number of the *London Magazine* for 1822, beginning a
spirited description of the Angerstein Gallery, now
happily included in our great National Collection.

At the end of 1822, after he had got his bit of *John
Buncleism*, as his grandson aptly describes his sham
Liber Amoris, off his hands, Hazlitt, with the undesir-
able Patmore as a companion, made a round of the
most famous picture collections in England — the
Angerstein, the Dulwich, and Lord Stafford's galleries,
those of Windsor Castle, Hampton Court, Wilton,
Stourhead, Petworth, Burleigh House, Fonthill Abbey,
and Blenheim, all of which he describes in fine style
in the *London Magazine* during the year 1823.

In these accounts we find Hazlitt himself again.
He is greatly enjoying himself, and goes his round in
search of pleasing sensations and ecstatic moments,
finding them in a ruff or a wrinkle of Rembrandt's, in
a portrait by Vandyke, in a Rubens or a Claude, in
Guidos, Correggios, and the Caracci. He took no

notes, feeling that he would rather make a mistake
now and then than spoil his whole pleasure in looking at a fine collection.   Hazlitt made many mistakes,
but he never spoilt his pleasure or ours.   Hazlitt is a
good critic of pictures in much the same way as he
is a good critic of books.   As one who had at least
tried to be a painter, he knew that much of the
painter's art is mechanical ; and as one who had worshipped the great masters of the art, perhaps only too
fiercely, he also knew how much was incommunicable.
Beyond this he took no great pains to qualify himself
as a critic of the Fine Arts.   He had read Richardson's book and Sir Joshua's and Flaxman's Discourses,
and Burke on "The Sublime and Beautiful," and
Hume on Taste, and had talked Art with Northcote
and Haydon ; but he had little of the hard student in
his composition, being always well content, with Lord
Foppington in one of his favourite plays, to rely upon
the sprouts of his own brain.

   Hazlitt excels in describing a picture ; and when, as
in the case of Titian's "Peter Martyr," the original
has been destroyed, a description by Hazlitt is a possession ; otherwise I do not know that an eloquent,
and probably in details inaccurate, description of a
picture is of much service.   It is the same thing with
descriptions of places in poetry — they are usually
failures the moment they descend to the particular
details.   Wordsworth can describe a glen, but not
Glencoe.

   The value of Hazlitt's art-criticism is that it disposes
you to be fond of pictures.   Mr. Gosse has well said :
" At a time when little attention was paid to art
criticism, when in England at least it was bound up

with an empty connoisseurship, and lost in the jargon
of the dilettante, it is the glory of Hazlitt that he
claimed for it the dignity of a branch of literature and
expended on it the wealth of his own fervid and
impassioned imagination." [1]

[1] See Preface to *Conversations of James Northcote*, edited by
Edmund Gosse. (R. Bentley and Son, 1894.)

CHAPTER IX

MAXIMS, TRAVELS, AND *THE SPIRIT OF THE AGE*

NOTHING was more characteristic of Hazlitt than the
attempt he made in this year 1823 to epitomise in a
series of sentences, maxims, or reflections, his philosophy of life. It is true that after a prolonged period of
stubbornness of mind and stiffness of pen, a period upon
which he looked back with an odd mixture of pride
and shame, he had now become one of the most fluent
of authors, and poured out his mind on a hundred
themes with abundant ease; but none the less, he
never lost his admiration for hard thinking and rocky
sentences. His own writings are full of outbursts of
eloquent reminiscence, of sentimental dreams, of autobiographical detail, but that is not the style he most
admired. What he loved best was the downright
unadorned honesty of purpose of Jonathan Edwards,
and the reticence that prevented Tucker from ever
mentioning the fact that by the time he came to write
the last volumes of the *Light of Nature pursued* he
was blind. "The golden mean," so Hazlitt writes,
"is indeed an exact description of the mode of life I
should like to live, and of the style I should like to
write, but, alas ! I am afraid I shall never succeed in
either object of my ambition." [1]

---

[1] *Tour in France and Italy.*

He says in the preface to the *Characteristics*, a small
book published anonymously, to escape abuse, in 1823,
that it was suggested by La Rochefoucauld, but it
jumped with his humour though alien to the style now
become his.   Hazlitt tried his best to squeeze his
humours into a narrow bed, to pen his flocking fancies
and prejudices into one fold.   His success is partial.
He could not keep his passion for Bonaparte or his
dislike of Pitt out of his maxims, which at times
run to a length unendurable in a maxim, however
praiseworthy in a sermon or commendable in an essay.

A few specimens shall be given of his gallant attempt, worthy of imitation by the whole quill-driving
fraternity, to cut himself short : —

"It is harder to praise a friend than an enemy.   By the
last we may acquire a reputation for candour; by the first
we only seem to discharge a debt."

"Society is a more level surface than we imagine.   Wise
men or absolute fools are hard to be met with, as there are
few giants or dwarfs.   The learned in books is ignorant
of the world; and he who is ignorant of books is often well
acquainted with other things, for life is of the same length
to all, and the mind cannot be idle."

"The study of metaphysics has this advantage at least —
it promotes an uprightness of understanding which is a cure
for the spirit of lying.   He who has devoted himself to the
discovery of truth feels neither pride nor pleasure in the invention of falsehood.   If you find a person given to vulgar
shifts and rhodomontade who at the same time tells you he is
a metaphysician, do not believe him."

"It is wonderful how soon men acquire talents for offices
of trust and importance.   We assume an equality with
circumstances."

"Men will die for an opinion as soon as for anything
else."

"We are only justified in rejecting prejudices when we

can explain the grounds of them, or when they are at war
with Nature, which is the strongest prejudice of all."

"It is a sign that real religion is in a state of decay
when passages in compliment of it are applauded at the
theatre."

"If the world were good for nothing else, it is a fine subject for speculation."

I have chosen eight out of four hundred and thirty-
four maxims or reflections, nor will their good quality
be denied. It is strange to think of the *Liber Amoris*
and the *Characteristics* appearing within a few months
of each other. Neither had any sale.

Although the cottages at Winterslow, which were
settled upon Mrs. Hazlitt, had been long exchanged
for an annuity payable to the lady during her life
(under a power, I presume, contained in the settlement), Hazlitt retained the habit of spending a good
deal of his time in the neighbourhood, his usual quar-
ters being an ancient inn known as "The Hutt," on
the Great Western Road. Close by were the woods of
Tudorsleigh and Clarendon. Stonehenge was within
a walk, and here Hazlitt's perturbed spirit found its
nearest approach to peace. He wrote much during his
later years at the Hutt, Winterslow.

In 1824 Hazlitt got married to a widow lady he
appears to have met for the first time in a stage coach,
and on a stage coach nobody could well be more
agreeable than Hazlitt. Very little is known of this
incident, not even the lady's maiden name. Her late
husband was a Colonel Bridgewater, who in his will
is described as of the island of Grenada, and by that
disposition left his widow Isabella £300 a year. As
the second Mrs. Hazlitt lived on till 1869, she was in

1824 probably a good deal younger than her new husband, then in his forty-seventh year.

When or where the marriage took place is not recorded, but on the 1st of September 1824 the couple left Brighton in the Dieppe packet. Hazlitt was essentially a man who lived by writing. Whatever he did, creditable or discreditable, wise or foolish, he put it first upon paper, and then upon the market. Accordingly, we have a full record of his travels in France and Italy made in the circumstances just narrated. Happily there are no love rhapsodies. The second Mrs. Hazlitt remains unsung, only one, and that the very barest, reference being made to her. The " Tour " first appeared in the *Morning Chronicle*, and was afterwards published in book form by Hunt and Clarke in 1826. There is no need to accuse Hazlitt of making mercenary marriages, for both his wives must have been economical dames if they did not spend all they had upon themselves. Hazlitt had always to scribble for his living. Had he had his own way, he would have been a country gentleman of good estate, retired habits, and philosophical opinions; writing in a style founded upon Arbuthnot's on the plagiarisms of Locke and Malthus and the true principles of human action; and fleeting away the time not so occupied in turning over old prints, devouring the Waverley Novels, and mooning about his shrubberies with Rousseau in one pocket and Congreve or Vanbrugh in another. But no such way of life was ever open to him, and no such snug retreat was ever to be his.

The Notes of a Journey through France and Italy is a manly, sensible, if perhaps a little drawn out, record of travel. Hazlitt dishes up his opinions and modes of

thought, whims and fancies, over and over again ; but
it is not easy to grow tired of them ; there is always
meat on his bones for the reader to consume.

His travels, like everything else he did with his pen,
are intensely literary. The style is excellent, but for
the truth you would not always vouch. Hazlitt's
description of his fellow-passengers on the steam-
packet, though lifelike, is not so convincing as Carlyle.
You do not feel sure they were on the boat : —

" We had a fine passage in the steamboat (Sept. 1, 1824).
Not a cloud, scarce a breath of air ; a moon, and then star-
light, till the dawn, with rosy fingers, ushered us into Dieppe.
Our fellow-passengers were pleasant and unobtrusive : an
English party of the better sort ; a member of Parliament,
delighted to escape from ' late hours and bad company ' ; an
English general, proud of his bad French ; a captain in the
navy, glad to enter a French harbour peaceably ; a country
squire, extending his inquiries beyond his paternal acres ; the
younger sons of wealthy citizens, refined through the strainers
of a university education, and finishing off with foreign
travel ; a young lawyer, quoting Peregrine Pickle, and
divided between his last circuit and projected tour. There
was also a young Dutchman, looking mild through his mus-
tachios, and a new married couple (a French Jew and Jew-
ess) who grew uxorious from the effects of sea-sickness, and
took refuge from the qualms of the disorder in paroxysms of
tenderness. We had some difficulty in getting into the
harbour, and had to wait till morning for the tide."

The first thing Hazlitt did on getting to Paris was
to hurry to the Louvre, there to be reminded of 1802,
when Bonaparte was First Consul, when the galleries
were full of " loot," and Hazlitt himself was to be a
painter.

" Oh ! for the change 'twixt Now and Then."

Still Hazlitt, as his wont was, enjoyed himself, even
though Bonaparte was dead, and Legitimacy squatted
like a toad in every corner of the gallery.   He searched
curiously for the pictures he had copied with such
feverish haste two-and-twenty years before.   Oddly
enough, some one else was wandering through the same
galleries searching for the same pictures, and bitterly
disappointed because she could not find them.   The
first Mrs. Hazlitt, ever fond of a jaunt, was also in
Paris, looking for "The Transfiguration" William had
copied.   The two met and renewed their chat.   This
Mrs. Hazlitt, writing home to her boy, then at school
in Tavistock, mentions that she had found his father
in Paris "splendidly situated" as to his rooms, in
"The Hôtel des Étrangers," Rue Vivienne, and getting
his food cooked in the English way, "which is a very
great object to him, but terribly expensive."   Hazlitt
confided to his former wife how Taylor and Hessey
would not give him what he wanted for the book of
travels he was writing, and that he meant to sell it to
the highest bidder on his return.   Mrs. Hazlitt also
tells the boy that his father had "talked of sending
him some money," but "found himself rather short."
No mention is made of the other Mrs. Hazlitt.

Hazlitt had now no affection for the French, who
had been content to forget Bonaparte and go back
like whipped dogs to the Bourbon kennels; and he
philosophises about their character, their poetry, their
drama, and their pictures in an unfriendly spirit.   He
positively prefers the English, of whom he remarks
with great point that their vanity does not heal the
wounds made in their pride, nor do they ever forgive
the men by whose corruption or stupidity those

wounds have been inflicted; but the French, he adds
with bitter significance, are soon reconciled to fate.
Even English cooking could not make Paris in 1824 a
pleasant place. Hazlitt had preached peace with
France, and now peace there was, but with a France
with whom he would be at war. On the whole, he
keeps his temper pretty well, though I doubt whether
a more venomous footnote was ever penned, even by a
commentator, than the one in which Hazlitt stabs his
brother-in-law, Dr. Stoddart, who is, à *propos* of nothing, suddenly informed that had he remained a revolutionary, he would probably have been as ridiculous
as he was as a renegade — "the great misfortune of a
certain class of persons being that they were ever born
or heard of."

Hazlitt's descriptions of Paris and Rome as those
cities were in 1824 are frank and vigorous. Paris, he
says bluntly, is a beast of a city to be in. There is
not a place, so he declared, where you can set your
foot in peace or comfort, unless you can take refuge in
one of their hotels, where you are locked up as in an
old-fashioned citadel, without any of the dignity of
romance.

"Fancy yourself in London with the footpath taken away,
so that you are forced to walk along the middle of the streets
with a dirty gutter running through them, fighting your way
through coaches, waggons, and hand-carts trundled along by
large mastiff-dogs, with the houses twice as high, greasy
holes for shop windows, and piles of wood, greenstalls, and
wheelbarrows placed at the doors, and the contents of wash-
hand basins pouring out of a dozen stories, — fancy all this
and worse, and, with a change of scene, you are in Paris.

"Paris is a vast pile of tall and dirty alleys, of slaughter-
houses and barbers' shops — an immense suburb huddled

together within the walls so close, that you cannot see the loftiness of the buildings for the narrowness of the streets, and where all that is fit to live in, and best worth looking at, is turned out upon quays, the boulevards, and their immediate vicinity."

Over the garden of the Tuileries he grows eloquent, but hardly as much as he does over — what think you? — the west end of London.

" But for a real West End, for a solid substantial *cut* into the heart of a metropolis, commend me to the streets and squares on each side of the top of Oxford Street, with Grosvenor and Portman Squares at one end, and Cavendish and Hanover at the other, linked together by Bruton, South Audley, and a hundred other fine old streets, with a broad, airy pavement, a display of comfort, of wealth, of taste, and rank all about you, each house seeming to have been the residence of some respectable old English family for half a century past, and with Portland Place, looking out towards Hampstead and Highgate, with their hanging gardens and lofty terraces, and Primrose Hill nestling beneath them, in green, pastoral luxury, the delight of the Cockneys, the aversion of Sir Walter and his merry men ! "

Rome cannot number Hazlitt among her victims.

" ' As London is to the meanest country town, so is Rome to every other city in the world.'

" So said an old friend of mine, and I believed him till I saw it.   This is not the Rome I expected to see.   No one from being in it would know he was in the place that had been twice mistress of the world.   I do not understand how Nicolas Poussin could tell, taking up a handful of earth, that it was ' a part of the ETERNAL CITY.'   In Oxford an air of learning breathes from the very walls ; halls and colleges meet your eye in every direction ; you cannot for a moment

forget where you are. In London there is a look of wealth
and populousness which is to be found nowhere else. In
Rome you are for the most part lost in a mass of tawdry,
fulsome *commonplaces*. It is not the contrast of pig-styes
and palaces that I complain of, the distinction between the
old and new ; what I object to is the want of any such
striking contrast, but instead an almost uninterrupted succession of narrow, vulgar-looking streets, where the smell of
garlic prevails over the odour of antiquity, with the dingy,
melancholy flat fronts of modern built houses, that seem in
search of an owner. A dunghill, an outhouse, the weeds
growing under an imperial arch offend me not ; but what
has a greengrocer's stall, a stupid English china warehouse,
a putrid *trattoria*, a barber's sign, an old clothes or old
picture shop, or a Gothic palace, with two or three lacqueys
in modern liveries lounging at the gate, to do with ancient
Rome? No ; this is not the wall that Romulus leaped
over ; this is not the Capitol where Julius Cæsar fell.
Instead of standing on seven hills, it is situated in a low
valley ; the golden Tiber is a muddy stream ; St. Peter's is
not equal to St. Paul's ; the Vatican falls short of the
Louvre, as it was in my time ; but I thought that here
were works immovable, immortal, inimitable on earth, and
lifting the soul half-way to heaven. I find them not, or only
what I had seen before in different ways. The stanzas of
Raphael are faded, or no better than the prints ; and the
mind of Michael Angelo's figures, of which no traces are to be
found in the copies, is equally absent from the walls of the
Sistine Chapel. Rome is great only in ruins : the Colosseum,
the Pantheon, the Arch of Constantine fully answered my
expectations ; and an air breathes round her stately avenues,
serene, blissful, like the mingled breath of spring and winter,
betwixt life and death, betwixt hope and despair. There is
little verdure, nor are any trees planted, on account of their
bad effects on the air. Happy climate ! in which shade and
sunshine are alike fatal. The Jews (I may add, while I
think of it) are shut up here in a quarter by themselves.
I see no reason for it. It is a distinction not worth the
making."

On St. Peter's he philosophises as follows: —

" After all, St. Peter's does not seem to me the chief boast
or most imposing display of the Catholic religion.   Old
Melrose Abbey, battered to pieces and in ruins, as it is,
impresses me much more than the collective pride and pomp
of Michael Angelo's great work.   Popery is here at home,
and may strut and swell and deck itself out as it pleases, on
the spot and for the occasion.   It is the pageant of an hour.
But to stretch out its arm fifteen hundred miles, to create a
voice in the wilderness, to have left its monuments standing
by the Teviot-side, or to send the midnight hymn through
the shades of Vallombrosa, or to make it echo among Alpine
solitudes, that is faith, and that is power.   The rest is a
puppet-show!   I am no admirer of Pontificals, but I am
a slave to the picturesque.   The priests talking together in
St. Peter's, or the common people kneeling at the altars,
make groups that shame all art.   The inhabitants of the
city have something French about them — something of the
cook's and the milliner's shop, something pert, gross, and
cunning; but the Roman peasants redeem the credit of their
golden sky.   The young women that come here from Gensano
and Albano, and that are known by their scarlet bodices
and white head-dresses and handsome good-humoured faces,
are the finest specimens I have ever seen of human nature.
They are like creatures that have breathed the air of heaven
till the sun has ripened them into perfect beauty, health, and
goodness.   They are universally admired in Rome.   The
Englishwomen that you see, though pretty, are pieces of
dough to them.   Little troops and whole families, men,
women, and children, from the Campagna and neighbouring
districts of Rome, throng the streets during Easter and
Lent, who come to visit the shrine of some favourite saint,
repeating their *Aves* aloud, and telling their beads with all
the earnestness imaginable.   Popery is no farce to them.
They surely think St. Peter's is the way to heaven.   You
even see priests counting their beads and looking grave.   If
they can contrive to get possession of this world for themselves, and give the laity the reversion of the next, were it

only in imagination, something is to be said for the exchange. I only hate half-way houses in religion or politics, that take from us all the benefits of ignorance and superstition, and give us none of the advantages of liberty or philosophy in return."

He was greatly irritated by the Stuart monument in St. Peter's. He was persuaded it never could have been put up without the consent of the Hanoverian dynasty, and that men who derived their title under the Act of Settlement should recognise Legitimacy was more than he could bear. "Is the dread of usurpation become so strong that a reigning family are half ready to acknowledge themselves usurpers in favour of those who are not likely to come back to assert their claim? We did not expel the slavish and tyrannical Stuarts from our soil to send a whining and Jesuitical recantation and writ of error after them to the other world a hundred years afterwards." If Hazlitt had lived to read Macaulay, he would have greatly rejoiced, though he must have condemned as a momentary lapse the touching lines of the historian on the Jacobite's grave in Rome, save so far indeed as even they contain some privy thrusts at the "slavish and tyrannical Stuarts."

Hazlitt, the man of sentiment, stands nakedly revealed in the comment he makes upon a story he repeats from M. Beyle's "charming little book entitled *L'Amour*." The story is that of the Madonna Pia referred to by Dante in the Fifth Canto of the *Purgatorio*, and the comment is as follows :—

" This story is interesting and well told. One such incident, or one page in Dante or in Spenser, is worth all the route between this and Paris, and all the sights in all

the post-roads in Europe. O Sienna! If I felt charmed
with thy narrow, tenantless streets, or looked delighted
through thy arched gateway over the subjected plain, it was
that some recollections of Madonna Pia hung upon the beat-
ings of my spirit, and converted a barren waste into the
regions of romance!"

The "Tour" concludes in a passage so much in the
very style of Mr. Froude as to make a sensitive reader
start and rub his eyes, which wander to where, in
their places, stand the *Short Studies:* —

"I confess London looked to me on my return like a
long, straggling, dirty country town; nor do the names
of Liverpool, Manchester, Birmingham, Leeds, or Coventry
sound like a trumpet in the ears, or invite our pilgrim steps
like those of Sienna, of Cortona, Perugia, Arezzo, Pisa, and
Ferrara. I am not sorry, however, that I have got back.
There is an old saying, *Home is home, be it never so homely.*
However delightful or striking the objects may be abroad,
they do not take the same hold of you, nor can you identify
yourself with them as at home. Not only is the language
an insuperable obstacle, other things as well as men speak a
language new and strange to you. You live comparatively
in a dream, though a brilliant and a waking one. It is in
vain to urge that you learn the language; that you are
familiarised with manners and scenery. No other language
can ever become our mother-tongue. We may learn the
words; but they do not convey the same feelings, nor is
it possible they should do so, unless we could begin our
lives over again, and divide our conscious being into two
different selves. Not only can we not attach the same
meaning to words, but we cannot see objects with the same
eyes, or form new loves and friendships after a certain period
of our lives. The pictures that most delighted me in Italy
were those I had before seen in the Louvre 'with eyes of
youth.' I could revive this feeling of enthusiasm, but not
transfer it. Neither would I recommend the going abroad

when young to become a mongrel being — half French, half
English.   It is better to be something than nothing.   It is
well to see foreign countries to enlarge one's speculative
knowledge and dispel false prejudices and libellous views
of human nature; but our affections must settle at home.
Besides, though a dream, it is a splendid one.   It is fine to
see the white Alps rise in the horizon of fancy at the
distance of a thousand miles ; or the imagination may wing
its thoughtful flight among the castellated Apennines, roaming from city to city over cypress and olive grove, viewing
the inhabitants as they crawl about mouldering palaces or
temples, which no hand has touched for the last three
hundred years, and see the genius of Italy brooding over
the remains of virtue, glory, and liberty, with Despair at
the gates, an English minister handing the keys to a foreign
despot, and stupid members of Parliament wondering what
is the matter ! "

Whilst in Florence, Hazlitt, attired in a dress-coat
and nankeen trousers half-way up his legs, leaving his
stockings well visible over his shoes, presented himself at the Palazzo Medici and demanded to see Landor,
an act of courage which excited the admiration and
aroused the fears of the English residents.   The two
men got on exceedingly well.   Hazlitt had reviewed
the first two volumes of the *Imaginary Conversations*
in the *Edinburgh;* and though he had, with all the
"spectacled gravity" of an austere critic, found his
author guilty of a strange lack of temper and decorum,
and full of arrogance and caprice, he had also greatly
delighted in many of the *Conversations*, and had written of them with feeling and enthusiasm.   Between
Hazlitt and Landor there were obvious resemblances.
Both hated kings far better than they loved peoples.
Neither of them was the least a democrat.   In fact,
the anti-Gallican phrensy which possessed the British

nation, and had so disgusted both Landor and Hazlitt, though Landor learned to alter his mind, was what the latter had once called it—"a drunken democracy." Popular wars, and wars usually are popular to begin with, are and must be democratic orgies. Landor, in a letter to Parr, once opined that there were, perhaps, thirty people then alive in the world to whom the word vulgar would not apply; and as for the public at large, why, there is not, wrote Hazlitt, "a more mean, stupid, dastardly, pitiful, selfish, spiteful, envious, ungrateful animal in existence." Both men had idolised Napoleon, who was referred to in Landor's *Gebir* (1798) as

" A mortal man beyond all mortal praise."

And though the line and the admiration that engendered it were both to disappear, Landor made up for his recantation by continuing to abuse all English ministers after a fashion far beyond the resources of Hazlitt's comparatively mild vocabulary. Both Hazlitt and Landor were in Paris in 1802 — the one as a poor artist, and the other as a man of fortune, but in very much the same temper of mind. Both men, despite their violent self-will, were saner politicians than were Southey and Wordsworth, either when "Society was their glittering bride" and "airy hopes their children"; or when, as Mr. Forster tersely puts it, they had made out their return journey from Utopia to Old Sarum. About Southey, whom Landor always loved, they might have quarrelled, had they not preferred to laugh, as also they might over Locke, for whom Landor entertained the greatest reverence. As critics, indeed, it would be hard to compare them.

Landor was a hundred times the better equipped and
caparisoned — a high priest of literature in costly
vestments — whilst Hazlitt may be compared to a
mendicant friar of prodigious eloquence, preaching
the joys of good books, good plays, and good
pictures.

The conversation between Landor and Hazlitt is
partly recorded in Landor's *Life* by Mr. Forster,
vol. ii. p. 207. It took an odd turn. The pair parted
in amity ; and Landor, with his accustomed profusion,
paid Hazlitt some very high compliments in the new
series of *Imaginary Conversations*, compliments afterwards struck out under the influence of Southey and
Julius Hare.

The "Tour" ended on the 16th of October 1825,
when Hazlitt and his son, who had joined his father
and stepmother somewhere *en route*, returned home
by way of St. Omer and Calais. Mrs. Hazlitt did not
come home with her husband, on whom she never set
eyes again. They parted peaceably ; but when, after
a fortnight, Hazlitt wrote to her in Switzerland,
inquiring when he should come over and escort her
back, she gave him to understand she was never
coming back. She went to live in Scotland, the
country to which she belonged by descent, and where
she died in September 1869. Hazlitt's grandson
thinks that his father, in 1825 a manly outspoken
little fellow, who took his mother's part, had something to do in making up the lady's mind to proceed
no further in the business.[1] Fortunately there is

---

[1] The lady may have been advised that her marriage was bigamous. (See note on p. 171.)

nothing written on either side. The subject was allowed to drop, and Hazlitt after his return home resumed life in London and at "The Hutt," Winterslow. By this time he was meditating upon a *Life of Napoleon.*

During the last few months of the "Tour" there had appeared in Colburn's *Magazine* — the new monthly — a periodical edited at different times, and always very badly, by Campbell, Bulwer, Hook, and Hood — a series of contemporary portraits called *The Spirit of the Age,* which, as all could see, though no name was added, were from the pen of Hazlitt. It was an alarming prospect, — full length characters or word-portraits of Coleridge, Southey, Wordsworth, Scott, Byron, Gifford, Bentham, Malthus, Campbell, etc., with descriptions of their manners and customs by the biting pen of Hazlitt, — who would not feel uneasy in handling such a volume for the first time? Happily *The Spirit of the Age,* Hazlitt's best book, as many think, is composed in a spirit, if not of Christian forgiveness, yet of a mellowed animosity. Hazlitt has not changed his mind or swerved an inch from the straight lines of his sinewy convictions (the expression is his own), but his temper is improved. It is only necessary to compare the Southey of the *Political Essays* with the Southey of *The Spirit of the Age* to observe the difference. There is something almost gracious in the latter essay, and the same holds good with regard to Coleridge and Wordsworth. Hazlitt was never petty and personal after De Quincey's fashion, but he was furious and reckless. He is no longer so in *The Spirit of the Age.* He was as much entitled to his opinions as any of the men he criticised

were to theirs. There was no earthly reason why he
should crook his knee to any of them, or why he
should abstain from unmasking the meanness of Gifford, or the essential intellectual poverty of Brougham;
but if it were done, it were well 'twere done good-
humouredly. To call *The Spirit of the Age* a good-
humoured book would be extravagant, but it is not a
book disfigured by passion and prejudice. The late
Mr. Gilfillan, an effusive and far from trustworthy
critic, but who yielded to none in his hearty enjoyment of a good book, used a happy phrase about *The
Spirit of the Age* when he called it the "Harvest
Home" of Hazlitt's mind. The reader of Hazlitt's
five-and-twenty volumes will discern most, if not all,
the significant thoughts and points of view with which
his reading has made him familiar, shining with an
undimmed light, and stated with unabated vigour in
The Spirit of the Age. I do not know whether the
Hazlitt beginner should begin or end with *The Spirit
of the Age;* there is much to be said on both sides;
but whether he begins or ends with it, he is a " barren
rascal" indeed if he does not enjoy it.

Two quotations, and they shall be good long ones,
will serve to illustrate the style and manner of these
incomparable sketches. I could equally well choose
two others. The Horne Tooke, for example, is a
superb portrait of the old Erastian, a type of man
well-nigh extinct; and it is really sad to think our
children will never see a true Erastian in the flesh, or
chuckle over his ingrained toughness of moral fibre.
The Cobbett is justly admired, and is as fine as a
portrait by Hogarth, but my two must be the Coleridge and the Scott.

This is the Coleridge : —

" ' Let us draw the curtain, and unlock the shrine.'

" Learning rocked him in his cradle, and while yet a child

' He lisped in numbers, for the numbers came.'

At sixteen he wrote his *Ode on Chatterton*, and he still reverts to that period with delight, not so much as it relates to himself (for that string of his own early promise of fame rather jars than otherwise), but as exemplifying the youth of a poet. Mr. Coleridge talks of himself without being an egotist, for in him the individual is always merged in the abstract and general. He distinguished himself at school and at the university by his knowledge of the classics, and gained several prizes for Greek epigrams. How many men are there (great scholars, celebrated names in literature) who, having done the same thing in their youth, have no other idea all the rest of their lives but of this achievement, of a fellowship and dinner, and who, installed in academic honours, would look down on the author as a mere strolling bard ! At Christ's Hospital, where he was brought up, he was the idol of those among his schoolfellows who mingled with their bookish studies the music of thought and of humanity ; and he was usually attended round the cloisters by a group of these (inspiring and inspired) whose hearts, even then, burnt within them as he talked, and where the sounds yet linger to mock ELIA on his way, still turning pensive to the past ! One of the finest and rarest parts of Mr. Coleridge's conversation is when he expatiates on the Greek tragedians (not that he is not well acquainted, when he pleased, with the epic poets, or the philosophers, or orators, or historians of antiquity) ; on the subtle reasonings and melting pathos of Euripides ; on the harmonious gracefulness of Sophocles, turning his love-laboured song, like sweetest warblings from a sacred grove ; on the high-wrought trumpet-tongued eloquence of Æschylus, whose Prometheus, above all, is like an Ode to Fate and a pleading with Providence, his thoughts being let loose as his body is chained on his solitary rock, and his afflicted will (the emblem of mortality)

> 'Struggling in vain with ruthless destiny.'

As the impassioned critic speaks and rises in his theme, you would think you heard the voice of the Man hated by the gods contending with the wild winds as they roar, and his eye glitters with the spirit of antiquity!

"Next, he was engaged with Hartley's tribes of mind, 'ethereal braid, thought-woven,' and he busied himself for a year or two with vibrations and vibratiuncles, and the great law of association that binds all things in its mystic chain, and the doctrine of Necessity (the mild teacher of Charity) and the Millennium, anticipative of a life to come, and he plunged deep into the controversy on matter and spirit; and, as an escape from Dr. Priestley's materialism, where he felt himself imprisoned by the logician's spell, like Ariel in the cloven pine-tree, he became suddenly enamoured of Bishop Berkeley's fairy-world,[1] and used in all companies to build the universe, like a brave poetical fiction, of fine words; and he was deep read in Malebranche, and in Cudworth's *Intellectual System* (a huge pile of learning, unwieldly, enormous), and in Lord Brooke's hieroglyphic theories, and in Bishop Butler's Sermons, and in the Duchess of Newcastle's fantastic folios, and in Clarke and South and Tillotson, and all the fine thinkers and masculine reasoners of that age; and Leibnitz's *Pre-established Harmony* reared its arch above his head, like the rainbow in the cloud, covenanting with the hopes of man; and then he fell plump, ten thousand fathoms down (but his wings saved him harmless), into the *hortus siccus* of Dissent, where he pared religion down to the standard of reason, and stripped faith of

---

[1] Mr. Coleridge named his eldest son (the writer of some beautiful sonnets) after Hartley, and the second after Berkeley. The third was called Derwent, after the river of that name. Nothing can be more characteristic of his mind than this circumstance. All his ideas indeed are like a river, flowing on for ever, and still murmuring as it flows, discharging its waters, and still replenished. [Hazlitt's own note.]

mystery, and preached Christ crucified and the Unity of the
Godhead, and so dwelt for a while in the spirit with John
Huss and Jerome of Prague and Socinus, and old John Zisca,
and ran through Neal's *History of the Puritans*, and Calamy's
Nonconformists' Memorial, having like thoughts and passions
with them. But then Spinoza became his God, and he took
up the vast chain of being in his hand, and the round world
became the centre and the soul of all things in some shadowy
sense, forlorn of meaning, and around him he beheld the
living traces and the sky-pointing proportions of the mighty
Pan ; but poetry redeemed him from his spectral philosophy,
and he bathed his heart in beauty, and gazed at the golden
light of heaven, and drank of the spirit of the universe, and
wandered at eve by fairy stream or fountain,

> '. . . When he saw nought but beauty,
> When he heard the voice of that Almighty One
> In every breeze that blew, or wave that murmured,'

and wedded with truth in Plato's shade, and in the writings
of Proclus and Plotinus saw the ideas of things in the eternal
mind, and unfolded all mysteries with the Schoolmen, and
fathomed the depths of Duns Scotus and Thomas Aquinas,
and entered the third heaven with Jacob Behmen, and walked
hand in hand with Swedenborg through the pavilions of the
New Jerusalem, and sung his faith in the promise and in the
word in his *Religious Musings ;* and lowering himself from
that dizzy height, poised himself on Milton's wings, and
spread out his thoughts in charity with the glad prose of
Jeremy Taylor, and wept over Bowles's *Sonnets*, and studied
Cowper's blank verse, and betook himself to Thomson's *Castle
of Indolence,* and sported with the wits of Charles the
Second's days and of Queen Anne, and relished Swift's style
and that of John Bull (Arbuthnot's we mean, not Mr.
Croker's), and dallied with the British essayists and novelists,
and knew all qualities of more modern writers with a learned
spirit — Johnson, and Goldsmith, and Junius, and Burke,
and Godwin, and the *Sorrows of Werter*, and Jean Jacques
Rousseau, and Voltaire, and Marivaux, and Crébillon, and

thousands more — now 'laughed with Rabelais in his easy
chair,' or pointed to Hogarth, or afterwards dwelt on Claude's
classic scenes, or spoke with rapture of Raphael, and compared the women at Rome to figures that had walked out of
his pictures, or visited the Oratory of Pisa, and described the
works of Giotto and Ghirlandajo and Massaccio, and gave
the moral of the picture of the ' Triumph of Death,' where the
beggars and the wretched invoke his dreadful dart, but the
rich and mighty of the earth quail and shrink before it ; and
in that land of siren sights and sounds saw a dance of peasant
girls, and was charmed with lutes and gondolas, or wandered
into Germany and lost himself in the labyrinths of the Hartz
Forest and of the Kantean philosophy, and among the cabal-
istic names of Fichte and Schelling and Lessing, and God
knows who.   This was long after, but all the former while
he had nerved his heart and filled his eyes with tears, as he
hailed the rising orb of liberty, since quenched in darkness
and in blood, and had kindled his affections at the blaze of
the French Revolution, and sang for joy when the towers of
the Bastille and the proud places of the insolent and the
oppressor fell, and would have floated his bark, freighted
with fondest fancies, across the Atlantic wave with Southey
and others to seek for peace and freedom —

'In Philharmonia's undivided dale ! '

Alas! 'Frailty, thy name is *Genius !* '   What is become of
all this mighty heap of hope, of thought, of learning, and
humanity?   It has ended in swallowing doses of oblivion
and in writing paragraphs in the *Courier.*   Such and so little
is the mind of man ! "—*The Spirit of the Age,* " Coleridge."

   Hazlitt's feeling for Scott is a crucial example of his
sanity as a critic.   Scott's politics were as abhorrent to
him as his to Scott.   He not unnaturally, however
mistakenly, thought Scott held shares in the " Blackwood Manufactory of Mischief."   Scott's " Charley
over the Waterism," and those subtle influences of his,
which are supposed by some thinkers to have had

their result in *The Christian Year, The Heir of Redclyffe,*
and the revival of the old nonjuring view of the
authority of the Episcopal Church, were, so far as
Hazlitt could dimly apprehend them, as anger-pro-
voking as the Stuart monument in St. Peter's. But
Scott's genius and humanity rode roughshod over all
Hazlitt's prejudices and passions. Even in the year
of Waterloo, which practically is also the year of
Waverley, Hazlitt became one of Sir Walter's men, and
to this day he remains by far his most interesting
critic. Others, Mr. Ruskin, for example, may have
uttered an occasional criticism going deeper into the
heart of things than Hazlitt's exhilarating approbation
may appear to do ; but I doubt whether Scott ever had
a reader with a finer eye for his best points or a truer
apprehension of his superb excellence, whilst I am
certain he has never had one so well able to impart
the warmth and glow of pleasure and delight.

It would be a blunder to regard the passage I am
about to quote as a mere roll-call of names, a pedigree
in which they all go on begetting one another to the
end of the chapter — it is a passage full of intimate
knowledge and intense joy, and every adjective is
selected with the finest taste.

" There is (first and foremost, because the earliest of our
acquaintance) the Baron of Bradwardine, stately, kind-hearted,
whimsical, pedantic ; and Flora MacIvor (whom even *we*
forgive for her Jacobitism), the fierce Vich Ian Vohr, and
Evan Dhu, constant in death, and Davie Gallatly roasting his
eggs or turning his rhymes with restless volubility, and the
two staghounds that met Waverley, as fine as ever Titian
painted, or Paul Veronese ; — then there is Old Balfour of
Burley, brandishing his sword and his Bible with fire-eyed

fury, trying a fall with the insolent, gigantic Bothwell at the
Change House, and vanquishing him at the noble battle of
Loudon Hill ; there is Bothwell himself, drawn to the life,
proud, cruel, selfish, profligate, but with the love letters of the
gentle Alice (written thirty years before), and his verses to
her memory, found in his pocket after his death ; in the same
volume of *Old Mortality* is that lone figure, like a figure in
Scripture, of the woman sitting on the stone at the turning to
the mountain, to warn Burley that there is a lion in his path ;
and the fawning Claverhouse, beautiful as a panther, smooth-
looking, blood-spotted ; and the fanatics, Macbriar and
Mucklewrath, crazed with zeal and sufferings ; and the in-
flexible Morton, and the faithful Edith, who refused to ' give
her hand to another while her heart was with her lover in the
deep and dead sea.'   And in *The Heart of Midlothian* we
have Effie Deans (that sweet, faded flower) and Jeanie, her
more than sister, and old Davie Deans, the patriarch of St.
Leonard's Crags, and Butler, and Dumbiedikes, eloquent in
his silence, and Mr. Bartoline Saddletree and his prudent
helpmate, and Porteous swinging in the wind, and Madge
Wildfire, full of finery and madness, and her ghastly mother.
Again, there is Meg Merrilies, standing on her rock, stretched
on her bier with ' her head to the east,' and Dirk Hatteraick
(equal to Shakespeare's Master Barnardine), and Glossin, the
soul of an attorney, and Dandie Dinmont, with his terrier
pack and his pony Dumple, and the fiery Colonel Mannering,
and the modish old counsellor Pleydell, and Dominie Samp-
son,[1] and Rob Roy (like the eagle in his eyry), and Bailie
Nicol Jarvie, and the inimitable Major Galbraith, and Rash-
leigh Osbaldistone, and Die Vernon, the best of secret keepers ;
and in the *Antiquary*, the ingenious and abstruse Mr. Jonathan Oldbuck, and the old beadsman Edie Ochiltree, and that
preternatural figure of old Edith Elspeth, a living shadow, in
whom the lamp of life had been long extinguished, had it not
been fed by remorse and ' thick-coming ' recollections ; and
that striking picture of the effects of feudal tyranny and

---

[1] Perhaps the finest scene in all these novels is that where the
Dominie meets his pupil, Miss Lucy, the morning after her brother's
arrival. [Hazlitt's own note, and a very fine one.]

fiendish pride, the unhappy Earl of Glenallan ; and the Black
Dwarf, and his friend Habbie of the Heughfoot (the cheerful
hunter), and his cousin Grace Armstrong, fresh and laughing
like the morning ; and the *Children of the Mist*, and the
baying of the bloodhound that tracks their steps at a distance (the hollow echoes are in our ears now), and Amy and
her hapless love, and the villain Varney, and the deep voice
of George of Douglas, and the immovable Balafre, and Master Oliver the Barber in *Quentin Durward*, and the quaint
humour of the *Fortunes of Nigel*, and the comic spirit of
Peveril of the Peak, and the fine old English romance of
Ivanhoe.   What a list of names !   What a host of associations !   What a thing is human life !   What a power is that
of genius !   What a world of thought and feeling is thus
rescued from oblivion !   How many hours of heartfelt satisfaction has our author given to the gay and thoughtless !
How many sad hearts has he soothed in pain and solitude !
It is no wonder that the public repay with lengthened applause
and gratitude the pleasure they receive.   He writes as fast as
they can read, and he does not write himself down.   He is
always in the public eye, and we do not tire of him.   His
worst is better than any other person's best.   His *backgrounds* (and his later works are little else but backgrounds
capitally made out) are more attractive than the principal
figures and most complicated actions of other writers.   His
works (taken together) are almost like a new edition of human
nature.   This is indeed to be an author ! " — *Spirit of the
Age*, "Sir Walter Scott."

This is an enthusiastic passage, and requires a *caveat*
to be entered.   Another quotation from a powerful
essay on "Scott, Racine, and Shakespeare," to be found
in the *Plain Speaker*, will serve this turn : —

" No one admires or delights in the Scotch Novels more
than I do ; but, at the same time, when I hear it asserted
that his mind is of the same class with Shakespeare's, or
that he imitates nature in the same way, I confess I cannot
assent to it.   No two things appear to me more different.

Sir Walter is an imitator of nature, and nothing more; but I think Shakespeare is infinitely more than this. The creative principle is everywhere restless and redundant in Shakespeare, both as it relates to the invention of feeling and imagery; in the author of *Waverley* it lies for the most part dormant, sluggish, and unused. Sir Walter's mind is full of information, but the '*o'er informing power*' is not there. Shakespeare's spirit, like fire, shines through him; Sir Walter's, like a stream, reflects surrounding objects. It is true, he has shifted the scene from Scotland into England and France, and the manners and characters are strikingly English and French; but this does not prove that they are not local, and that they are not borrowed, as well as the scenery and costume, from comparatively obvious and mechanical sources. Nobody from reading Shakespeare would know (except from the *Dramatis Personæ*) that Lear was an English king. He is merely a king and a father. The ground is common; but what a well of tears has he dug out of it! The tradition is nothing, or a foolish one. There are no data in history to go upon; no advantage is taken of costume, no acquaintance with geography, or architecture, or dialect is necessary; but there is an old tradition, human nature — an old temple, the human mind — and Shakespeare walks into it and looks about him with a lordly eye, and seizes on the sacred spoils as his own. The story is a thousand or two years old, and yet the tragedy has no smack of antiquarianism in it. I should like very well to see Sir Walter giving us a tragedy of this kind, a huge 'globose' of sorrow, swinging round in mid-air, independent of time, place, and circumstance, sustained by its own weight and motion, and not propped up by the levers of custom, or patched up with quaint, old-fashioned dresses, or set off by grotesque backgrounds or rusty armour, but in which the mere paraphernalia and accessories were left out of the question, and nothing but the soul of passion and the pith of imagination was to be found. 'A dukedom to a beggarly *denier*,' he would make nothing of it. Does this prove he has done nothing, or that he has not done the greatest things? No, but that he is not like Shakespeare."

CHAPTER X

THE first time the *Life of Napoleon* is heard of is from
Captain Medwin, often called the friend of Byron, and
a man given to printing in the magazines conversations
he reported himself to have had with well-known
persons he encountered by the way. Hazlitt had
lingered some time at Vevey, where, sitting though
he was in the open air, Clarens on his left, behind
him

"The cone of Jaman pale and grey,"

the rocks of Meillerie opposite, white and purple
flowers at his feet, he wrote a downright, honest,
John Bullish essay called "Merry England," in which
he extols fox-hunting, and declares that the coloured
prints and pictures depicting the chase in all its humours and incidents, to be seen hanging up in old halls
and ale-houses, "have more life and health and spirit
in them, and mark the pith and nerve of the national
character more creditably than the mawkish, sentimental, affected designs of Theseus and Pirithous, and
Æneas and Dido, pasted on foreign *salons à manger* and
the interior of country houses"; and at Vevey it was
he met Captain Medwin.

What Hazlitt said to Medwin was this: "I will

write a *Life of Napoleon*, though it is yet too early; some have a film before their eyes, some want magnifying-glasses, none see him as he is in true proportions." Hazlitt kept his word and wrote a *Life of Napoleon* in four stout volumes.

The public is certainly ungrateful, even if it does not deserve all the other epithets Hazlitt heaped upon it. It clamours for big books from those who write small ones, and seldom fails to point out to the author of a big book how much wiser he would have been had he written a small one. Even Mr. Leslie Stephen concludes an essay on Hazlitt (in whom he delights) by expressing a regret that so vigorous a writer has not left some more enduring monument of his remarkable powers. Hazlitt worked his hardest to build a monument, and it is not his fault that his *Life of Napoleon* has not endured. How could he, out of the materials to his hand, write a *Life of Napoleon* in four volumes it would be worth anybody's while to read to-day? The thing was not to be done in 1826 either by Scott or Hazlitt. Big books seldom live long, and the importance attached to them is misleading. Histories and philosophies stand a poor chance with *Barbara S.*, the *Confessions of an Opium Eater*, and a description of John Cavanagh playing fives. Had Charles Lamb written a *History of the Elizabethan Drama* instead of the *Essays of Elia*, De Quincey the *Principles of Political Economy*, and no *Autobiographical Sketches*, and Hazlitt nothing but the *Life of Napoleon*, how many people to-day would know more than the sound of their names — if indeed so much as that? In literature nothing counts but genius; and between a work of genius however small and a task of utility however long, there is a greater gulf fixed than there is between *Dream Children* and the *Faerie Queen.*

Hazlitt on his return to England divided his time between Winterslow and his lodging in London, which was now in that West End for which he expressed such admiration — first in Down Street, and afterwards at 40 Half Moon Street. He had to work hard for his living, contributing to the *Edinburgh Review* and the *New Monthly*, the *Atlas*, the *Examiner*, the *Morning Chronicle*, and the *London Weekly Review.* His average income, his son says, was somewhere about £600 a year; but it all had to be made from day to day.

The *Plain Speaker*, two more volumes of miscellaneous essays, contributed to the *London Magazine* and other papers, appeared in 1826. What was said of the *Table-Talk* volumes may with equal truth be said of these. If they are not the very perfection of miscellaneous writing, they come very near it. [1]

I have already quoted a passage on the Orator, taken from the essay on " Writing and Speaking " which appeared in the *Plain Speaker*, and I will now take from the same essay the companion-picture of the Writer : —

" The writer must be original, or he is nothing. He is not to take up with ready-made goods ; for he has time allowed him to create his own materials, to make novel com-

---

[1] In the *Plain Speaker* are to be found the essay on the ' Spirit of Obligations' (which Mr. R. L. Stevenson, for some unexplained reason, found epoch-making) ; the essay on ' Egotism,' full of the finest criticism; the essay entitled 'The New School of Reform,' an eloquent defence of Sentimentalism, and other of Hazlitt's most famous performances. ' It is of this finer essence of wisdom and humanity, " ethereal mould, sky-tinctured," that books of the better sort are made.' — Essay on the *Conversation of Authors.*

binations of thought and fancy, to contend with unforeseen difficulties of style and execution, while we look on and admire the growing work in secret and at leisure.   There is a degree of finishing as well as of solid strength in writing, which is not to be got at every day, and we can wait for perfection.   The author owes a debt to truth and nature which he cannot satisfy at sight, but he has pawned his head on redeeming it.   It is not a string of clap-traps to answer a temporary or party purpose — violent, vulgar, and illiberal — but general and lasting truth that we require at his hands. We go to him as pupils, not as partisans.   We have a right to expect from him profounder views of things ; finer observations ; more ingenious illustrations ; happier and bolder expressions.   He is to give the choice and picked results of a whole life of study, what he has struck out in his most felicitous moods, has treasured up with most pride, has laboured to bring to light with most anxiety and confidence of success. He may turn a period in his head fifty different ways, so that it comes out smooth and round at last.   He may have caught a glance of a simile, and it may have vanished again ; let him be on the watch for it, as the idle boy watches for the lurking-place of the adder.   We can wait.   He is not satisfied with a reason he has offered for something ; let him wait till he finds a better reason.   There is some word, some phrase, some idiom that expresses a particular idea better than any other, but he cannot for the life of him recollect it : let him wait till he does.   Is it strange that among twenty thousand words in the English language, the one of all others that he most needs should have escaped him ?   There are more things in nature than there are words in the English language, and he must not expect to lay rash hands on them all at once.

> 'Learn to *write* slow ; all other graces
> Will follow in their proper places.'

"You allow a writer a year to think of a subject; he should not put you off with a truism at last.   You allow him a year more to find out words for his thoughts; he should not give us an echo of all the fine things that have been said a hundred times."

What are called *Hazlitt's Select Poets* is a compilation
made whilst Hazlitt was abroad, it is commonly supposed by Procter, aided by Lamb, and it may be one
or two others, who worked upon a copy of *Chalmers's
Poets* belonging to, or at all events borrowed from,
Leigh Hunt, who had good reason to complain of the
state the volumes were in when the anthologists had
completed their task of selection. I too have seen
anthologists at work. Wordsworth's lines on "Nut-
ting" feebly convey their method. The original plan
of the selection included *Living Poets*, and one copy at
least so complete got into circulation, but the living poets or their publishers foolishly objected, and the
edition was rigorously suppressed, and the volume
now to be seen on the bookstalls contains only poets
who were " in their misery dead " in 1825.

The notes are marvels of terseness, and, I should
judge, Hazlitt's own. An example or two may be
given : —

"MARVELL is a writer almost forgotten, but undeservedly
so. His poetical reputation seems to have sunk with his
political party. His satires were coarse, quaint, and virulent ;
but his other productions are full of a lively, tender, and
elegant fancy. His verses leave an echo on the ear and
find one in the heart. See those entitled ' Bermudas,' ' To his
Coy Mistress,' ' On the Death of a Fawn,' " etc.

"DRYDEN stands nearly at the head of the second class
of English poets, viz. the *artificial*, or those who describe
the mixed modes of artificial life and convey general precepts
and abstract ideas. He had invention in the plan of his
Satires, very little fancy, not much wit, no humour, immense
strength of character, elegance, masterly ease, indignant contempt approaching to the sublime, not a particle of tender-

ness, but eloquent declamation, the perfection of uncorrupted English style, and of sounding, vehement, varied versification. The *Alexander's Feast*, his *Fables*, and *Satires* are his standard and lasting works."

" Collins, of all our minor poets, that is, those who have attempted only short pieces, is probably the one who has shown the most of the highest qualities of poetry, and who excites the most intense interest in the bosom of the reader. He soars into the regions of imagination, and occupies the highest peaks of Parnassus.   His fancy is glowing, vivid, but at the same time hasty and obscure.   Gray's sublimity was borrowed and mechanical compared to Collins's, who has the true inspiration, the *vivida vis* of the poet.   He heats and melts objects in the fervour of his genius as in a furnace. See his Odes ' To Fear,' ' On the Poetical Character,' and ' To Evening.'   The ' Ode on the Passions ' is the most popular, but the most artificial of his principal ones.   His qualities were fancy, sublimity of conception, and no mean degree of pathos, as in the *Eclogues* and *The Dirge in Cymbeline*."

" Young is a poet who has been much overrated from the popularity of his subject and the glitter and lofty pretensions of his style.   I wished to have made more extracts from the *Night Thoughts*, but was constantly repelled by the tinsel of expression, the false ornaments, and laboured conceits.   Of all writers who have gained a great name, he is the most meretricious and objectionable.   His is false wit, false fancy, false sublimity, and mock tenderness.   At least, it appears so to me." [1]

During 1826 and 1827, whilst the *Napoleon* was in preparation, and getting itself written chiefly at Winterslow, Hazlitt committed his last indiscretion. He began publishing in the *New Monthly* what pur-

---

[1] "Hazlitt's Poets is the best selection I have ever seen."—*Edward FitzGerald* (1832).

ported to be, and partly was, the record of conversations between old James Northcote, then about eighty
years old, and himself.   The articles were signed
" Boswell Redivivus " ; and contained, as they naturally did, whether proceeding from Northcote's lips or
Hazlitt's pen, many free-spoken remarks about other
people.   They excited attention ; and the old painter,
who was really much pleased with the interest he occasioned, pretended to be furious, and the editor — the
poet Campbell, his old wound still smarting — declared
himself disgusted.   Northcote had his remedy — to
shut his door in Hazlitt's face and let the world know
he had done so — but he had no mind to do this, and
Hazlitt continued to publish the conversations, which
were afterwards printed in the book known as *The
Conversations of James Northcote, Esq., R.A.,* 1830.
Somebody has said that all the ill-nature in this book
is Northcote's, and all, or almost all, the talent Hazlitt's.
It is impossible to partition it on any such principle.
Both Northcote and Hazlitt were well supplied with
both the qualities in question.   It is, however, obvious
to the reader who knows Hazlitt, that he has not hesitated to make the painter say what either Hazlitt did
actually say in the course of conversation, or what he
wrote afterwards out of his own head.   He had no
scruples in such matters.   For Northcote, however, he
had a genuine respect and a strange kind of admiration.   He envied him the head upon his shoulders and
his " agreeable old age."   In his letter to his son " On
the Conduct of Life," a great performance, full of
wisdom and feeling, Hazlitt writes : —

" Yet if I were to name one pursuit rather than another,
I should wish you to be a good painter, if such a thing could

be hoped.   I have failed in this myself, and should wish you
to be able to do what I have not — to paint like Claude,
or Rembrandt, or Guido, or Vandyke, if it were possible.
Artists, I think, who have succeeded in their chief object live
to be old, and are agreeable old men.   Their minds keep alive
to the last.   Cosway's spirits never flagged till after ninety ;
and Nollekens, though nearly blind, passed all his mornings
in giving directions about some group or bust in his workshop.
You have seen Mr. Northcote, that delightful specimen of the
last age.   With what avidity he takes up his pencil, or lays
it down again to talk of numberless things !   His eye has not
lost its lustre, nor 'paled its ineffectual fire.'   His body is a
shadow ; he himself is a pure spirit.   There is a kind of
immortality about this sort of ideal and visionary existence
that dallies with Fate and baffles the grim monster — Death.
If I thought you could make as clever an artist and arrive
at such an agreeable old age as Mr. Northcote, I should
declare at once for your devoting yourself to this enchanting
profession ; and in that reliance, should feel less regret at
some of my own disappointments, and little anxiety on your
account ! "

An edition of the *Conversations*, with critical remarks
upon Hazlitt as a judge of art by Mr. Gosse, has
lately appeared, and should be referred to. Although
Hazlitt shows no diminution of what may be called
his literary high spirits, he was now in bad health,
and becoming familiar with the environment of the
sick-chamber.

By the end of 1827 two volumes of the *Napoleon*
were ready for the printers. Messrs. Hunt and Cowden Clarke were to be the publishers; and as the time
approached for publication, Hazlitt, unaccustomed as
he was to so big a book, grew fidgety and nervous.
The passion of a lifetime was involved. It cost him
nothing to discourse about poetry and the drama, or
to rhapsodise about Rousseau, Mrs. Siddons, or Titian

— such writing flowed from his brain — it was, he says, like a girl copying a sampler, but Bonaparte was another matter.   He well knew the prejudice he had to encounter, and he must have known how ill equipped he was to encounter it.   Scott's *Life* had already taken the field with all the *éclat* of a great name and the weight of the national position behind it.   The false Duessa sat enthroned — how could he hope to unmask her horrors to the world ?   His spirits failed him, his heart sank.   He wrote a preface, and he piqued himself upon his prefaces, which in fact were essays, and lent themselves to the style he had mastered.   In this preface he tells us why he wrote the book.   His first object was to make it plain that Bonaparte stood alone between the legitimate kings and their ancient prey — mankind.   As for Napoleon's faults — great as they were — they had this novelty about them, that they did not (so Hazlitt asserts) proceed upon the principle that "the millions were made for one" ; and so long as this was the case, why, then, he cries triumphantly, "liberty was saved and the Revolution untouched."   Hofer would hardly have assented to this "abstract principle," but there is now no need to argue the point ; and, indeed, just now Hofers are out of fashion in an age which demands bigness at all costs.

"There were," Hazlitt proceeds to say in his preface, "two other feelings that influenced me on the subject — a love of *glory*, when it did not interfere with other things, and the wish to see personal merit prevail over external rank and circumstance.   I felt pride (not envy) to think that there was one reputation in modern times equal to the ancients, and at seeing one man greater than the throne he sat upon."

This is not Whig doctrine, and indeed is quite contrary to the principles of 1688.

For some reasons the publishers were afraid of the preface, and it was for a while kept back. One of Hazlitt's rare letters to a publisher relates to the subject : —

"DEAR SIR, — I thought all the world agreed with me at present that Bonaparte was better than the Bourbons, or that a tyrant was better than tyranny. In my opinion, no one of an understanding above the rank of a lady's waiting-maid could ever have doubted this, though I alone said it ten years ago. It might be impolicy then and now for what I know, for the world sticks to an opinion in appearance long after they have given it up in reality. I should like to know whether the preface is thought impolitic by some one who agrees with me in the main point, or by some one who differs with me and makes this excuse not to have his opinion contradicted? In Paris (*jubes regina renovare dolorem*) the preface was thought a masterpiece, the best and only possible defence of Bonaparte, and quite new *there!* It would be an impertinence in me to write a *Life of Bonaparte* after Sir W.[1] without some such object as that expressed in the preface. After all, I do not care a *damn* about the preface. It will get me on four pages somewhere else. Shall I retract my opinion altogether and foreswear my own book? The remainder of vol. ii. will be ready to go on with, but not the beginning to the third. The appendixes had better be at the end of second vol. Pray get them if you can : you have my Sieyes, have you not? One of them is there. I have been nearly in the other world. My regret was to 'die and leave the world "rough" copy.' Otherwise I had thought of an epitaph and a good end : ' Hic jacent reliquiæ mortales Gulielmi Hazlitt, auctoris non intelligibilis : natus Maidstoniæ in comi(ta)tu Cantiæ, Apr. 10, 1778. Obiit Winterslowe, Dec. 1827.' I think

[1] Sir Walter Scott.

of writing an epistle to C. Lamb, Esq., to say that I have passed near the shadowy world, and have had new impressions of the vanity of this, with hopes of a better. Don't you think this would be good policy? Don't mention it to the severe author of the *Press*, a poem,[1] but methinks the idea *arridet Hone*. He would give sixpence to see me floating upon a pair of borrowed wings half-way between heaven and earth, and edifying the good people at my departure, whom I shall only scandalise by remaining. At present my study and contemplation is the leg of a stewed fowl. I have behaved like a saint, and been obedient to orders.

" *Non fit pugil*, etc. I got a violent spasm by walking fifteen miles in the mud, and getting into a coach with an old lady who would have the window open. Delicacy, moderation, complaisance, the *suaviter in modo*, whisper it about, my dear Clarke, these are my faults, and have been my ruin. — Yours ever,   W. H.

" December 7, 1827.
" I can't go to work before Sunday or Monday. By then the doctor says he shall have made a new man of me.
" Pray how's your sister?
" C. Cowden Clarke, Esq."

The first two volumes appeared in 1828, and attracted hardly any notice. Mr. Fonblanque, a competent and independent critic, praised the book very warmly in the friendly columns of the *Examiner;* but his praise could not compensate either for the general indifference of the public or the pecuniary embarrassment of the publishers, who were not in a position to pay even the miserable sum Hazlitt had agreed to take as the price of his labour.

Stricken in health, and now feeling for the first time the actual pinch of poverty, Hazlitt grimly con-

---

[1] Mr. M'Cleery the printer.

tinued working at the *Life*, and keeping the wolf from the door by writing for the periodicals. His London lodgings were by this time in Bouverie Street, and here he wrote for the *Edinburgh Review* two articles — one on Flaxman's lectures on Sculpture, the other on Wilson's *Life of De Foe*. Lamb, writing to Wilson in November 1829, refers to Hazlitt's intention, mournfully adding, "I wish I had health and spirits to do it." Hazlitt was not well supplied with either commodity, but he was a dauntless fellow.

The two concluding volumes of the *Napoleon* were published by Effingham Wilson in 1830, so there was an end of that job. The *Life* excited the genuine admiration of so good a judge of a book as Talfourd, who calls it a splendid work, its style glowing with the fervour of battle and stiffening with the spoils of victory. But there was nothing lasting about it; and the passion for Bonaparte, not unpleasing in the essayist and sentimentalist, becomes rancid in the historian. We prefer history to be written by those who know — if they feel too, so much the better; but the more knowledge they have, the better chance they have of being read.

Hazlitt's failure was no greater than Scott's; and of the two *Lives*, Hazlitt's is by far the more spirited; whilst in Fonblanque's language "it exhibits a deeper insight into the sources of principles, of morals and politics, than nine out of ten of the formal treatises which are regarded as profound authority." The tameness of Scott's *Life* is unbearable.

One quotation from Hazlitt's *Napoleon* will show that he possessed undeniable qualifications to write about the Revolution: —

"It has been sometimes pretended as if the French Revolution burst out like a volcano, without any previous warning, only to alarm and destroy, or was one of those comet-like appearances, the approach of which no one can tell till the shock and conflagration are felt. What is the realstate of the case? There was not one of those abuses and grievances which the rough grasp of the Revolution shook to air that had not been the butt of ridicule, the theme of indignant invective, the subject of serious reprobation for near a century. They had been held up without ceasing and without answer to the derision of the gay, the scorn of the wise, the sorrow of the good. The most witty, the most eloquent, the most profound writers were unanimous in their wish to remove or reform these abuses, and the most dispassionate and well-informed part of the community joined in the sentiment; it was only the self-interested or the grossly ignorant who obstinately clung to them. Every public and private complaint had been subjected to the touchstone of inquiry and argument; the page of history, of fiction, of the drama, of philosophy had been laid open, and their contents poured into the public ear, which turned away disgusted from the arts of sophistry or the menace of authority. It was this operation of opinion, enlarging its circle, and uniting nearly all the talents, the patriotism, and the independence of the country in its service, that brought about the events which followed. Nothing else did or could. It was not a dearth of provisions, the loss of the queen's jewels, that could overturn all the institutions and usages of a great kingdom; it was not the Revolution that produced the change in the face of society, but the change in the texture of society that produced the Revolution, and brought its outward appearance into a nearer correspondence with its inward sentiments. There is no other way of accounting for so great and sudden a transition."

The completed work had no sale; and owing to Hunt and Clarke's failure to meet their obligations, brought its author nothing. He was to have had

£500; he got a bill for £140, and the bill was waste-paper. He called an accountant to his assistance, and the accountant turned out to be a rogue, and added to his embarrassments and misery. Hazlitt moved into his last lodging, No. 6 Frith Street, Soho, at the beginning of 1830, and here he was attacked with a gastric inflammation.

Mr. Reynell (whose daughter became the wife of Hazlitt's son, now nineteen years of age) came to see his old friend after the Revolution in France of July 1830, but not even the downfall of the Bourbons could raise Hazlitt's spirits. "I'm afraid, Charles," said he, "things will go back again." There is no peace for the politician save in the grave, and thitherward Hazlitt was now fast tending.

On his hearing that his son was likely to marry Miss Reynell, he was much pleased, and in June 1830 we find Charles Lamb being consulted by the boy's mother (who was at Buxton for her rheumatism) as to whether Hazlitt would consent to his son's studying music, as he had a fine voice. Lamb saw Hazlitt on this subject, and reports that he expressed "such horror and aversion" to his son's singing in public that Lamb felt he could not meddle further in the matter.

Hazlitt continued writing to the last, and did muster up spirit to compose a paper on the deposition of Charles the Tenth. His two lasts essays are called "The Free Admission" and "The Sick Chamber."

Through the months of August and September he continued the struggle with Death. He longed to see his mother, and begged that she might be sent for; but she was eighty-four years old, down in Devonshire, and could not come. Procter describes him in dire straits. His mind was clear and strong. He died on the 18th of September 1830. His last words were unexpected, but we may be sure sincere: "Well, I've had a happy life."

Charles Lamb, Mr. White, Mr. Hessey, and the younger Hazlitt were in the room when he died. Mr. R. H. Horne, Mr. Patmore, Mr. Basil Montagu, and Mr. Wells, the author of *Joseph and his Brethren,* all seem to have been attentive to the wants of the dying man.

Of money there certainly was no superfluity. Jeffrey, hearing of his old contributor's plight, sent £50, which did not reach the house till Hazlitt was dead; but though his circumstances were bad, he was not in want. No friend of Charles Lamb's ever was.

"All his wants," so wrote his son, "were carefully studied, and at the time of his death he was amply provided with everything which could be required."

It is impossible not to notice that this is a guarded mode of expression.

Dr. Darling, a physician well known in connection with the class of complaint, a kind of cholera, from which Hazlitt suffered, attended him with the utmost assiduity; and if there were those among the laity who conceived him to misunderstand the case, the circumstance would not be unusual.

Hazlitt was buried in the Churchyard of St. Anne's, Soho, and here admirers, not a few, have sought out his grave, and spelt through the terribly long, but not wholly uncharacteristic, epitaph which Mr. R. H. Horne was allowed to inscribe on the tombstone. This epitaph, which may still be read in the *Literary Remains*, is no longer on the stone, which is now removed from its former site, and bears upon its face the following words : —

" On the northern side of this ground lie the remains of William Hazlitt, Painter, Critic, Essayist.
Born at Maidstone, April 10, 1778.
Died in Soho, September 18, 1830.
Restored by his grandson.
Feb. 1901."

It was Hazlitt's good fortune to enjoy the friend-ship of one of the kindliest of his contemporaries, Mr. Serjeant, afterwards Mr. Justice, Talfourd. There are those still living, and among them Lord James of Hereford and Sir Henry Poland, who well remember the pleasant and miscellaneous parties that used to meet, and the kindness that was disseminated under the roof of this hospitable, delightful, and accom-plished man. Talfourd's " Thoughts upon the late William Hazlitt," to be found in the *Literary Remains*, are, and will probably always remain, the best account of the difficult personality with whom they were con-cerned. They should be read in their proper place and in their entirety ; but Talfourd's description of Hazlitt's personal appearance must be given : —

" In person, Mr. Hazlitt was of the middle size, with a handsome and eager countenance, worn by sickness and thought, and dark hair, which had curled stiffly over the temples, and was only of late years sprinkled with grey. His gait was slouching and awkward, and his dress neglected ; but when he began to talk, he could not be mistaken for a common man. In the company of persons with whom he was not familiar his bashfulness was painful; but when he became entirely at ease, and entered on a favourite topic, no one's conversation was ever more delightful. He did not talk for effect, to dazzle, or surprise, or annoy, but with the most simple and honest desire to make his view of the subject entirely apprehended by his hearer. There was sometimes an obvious struggle to do this to his own satisfaction; he seemed labouring to bring his thought to light from its deep lurking-place; and, with modest distrust of that power of expression which he had found so late in life, he often betrayed a fear that he had failed to make himself understood, and recurred to the subject again and again, that he might be assured he had succeeded. In argument he was candid and liberal; there was nothing about him pragmatical or exclusive; he never drove a principle to its utmost possible consequences, but, like Locksley, 'allowed for the wind.' For some years previous to his death he observed an entire abstinence from fermented liquors, which he had once quaffed with the proper relish he had for all the good things of this life, but which he courageously resigned when he found the indulgence perilous to his health and faculties. The cheerfulness with which he made this sacrifice always appeared to us one of the most amiable traits in his character. He had no censure for others who, with the same motive, were less wise or less resolute; nor did he think he had earned, by his own constancy, any right to intrude advice which he knew, if wanted, must be unavailing. Nor did he profess to be a convert to the general system of abstinence which was advocated by one of his kindest and staunchest friends; he avowed that he yielded to necessity; and instead of avoiding the sight of that which he could no longer taste, he was seldom so happy as when he sat with friends at their wine, participating the sociality of the time, and renewing his own past enjoyment in that of his companions, without regret and without envy. Like Dr. Johnson, he made himself a poor amends for the loss of wine by drinking tea, not so largely, indeed, as the hero of Boswell, but at least of equal potency, for he might have

challenged Mrs. Thrale and all her sex to make stronger tea
than his own.   In society, as in politics, he was no flincher.
He loved ' to hear the chimes at midnight ' without consider-
ing them as a summons to rise.   At these seasons, when in
his happiest mood, he used to dwell on the conversational
powers of his friends, and live over again the delightful hours
he had passed with them ; repeat the pregnant puns that one
had made ; tell over again a story with which another had
convulsed the room, or expand in the eloquence of a third ;
always best pleased when he could detect some talent which
was unregarded by the world, and giving alike, to the celebrated and the unknown, due honour."

Mr. Procter speaks of Hazlitt's quick, restless, grey
eyes, his solitary habits, black hair, sprinkled with
grey, slovenly dress at home, but neat when he went
abroad, his mode of walking loose and unsteady,
although his arms displayed strength when playing
rackets with Martin Burney and others.

Mr. Patmore, who plays a dubious part in Hazlitt's
life, is more lurid than the amiable Procter, and speaks
of "fearful indications of internal passion" and "truly
awful" expressions of face when offended, but he proceeds : —

"When in good health, and in a tolerable humour with
himself and the world, his face was more truly and entirely
answerable to the intellect that spoke through it than any
other I ever saw, either in life or on canvas ; and its crowning
portion, the brow and forehead, was, to my thinking, quite
unequalled for mingled capacity and beauty. . . .   The mouth,
from its ever-changing form and character, could scarcely be
described, except as to its astonishingly varied power of
expression, which was equal to, and greatly resembled, that
of Edmund Kean. . . .   He always lived (during the period
of my intimacy with him) in furnished lodgings. . . .   He
usually rose at from one to two o'clock in the day, scarcely

ever before twelve ; and if he had no work in hand, he would
sit over his breakfast (of excessively strong black tea and
a toasted French roll) till four or five in the afternoon — silent,
motionless, and self-absorbed, as a Turk over his opium pouch,
for tea served him precisely in this capacity.   It was the only
stimulant he ever took, and at the same time the only luxury ;
the delicate state of his digestive organs prevented him from
tasting any fermented liquors, or touching any food but beef
or mutton, or poultry, or game. . . . A cup of his tea (if you
happened to come in for the first brewage of it) was a peculiar
thing ; I have never tasted anything like it.   He always made
it himself, using with it a great quantity of sugar and cream.
To judge from its occasional effects upon myself, I should say
that the quantity he drank of this tea produced ultimately
a most injurious effect upon him. . . . His breakfast and tea
were frequently the only meals that he took till late at night,
when he usually ate a hearty supper of hot meat.   This he
invariably took at a tavern." — Patmore's *Friends and
Acquaintances*, vol. ii. pp. 302–8.

Hazlitt was accustomed, says his grandson, writing
from family tradition, "to speak low like Coleridge,
with his chin bent and his eyes widely expanded, and
his voice and manner as a rule were apt to communi-
cate an impression of querulousness, and the tone was
of a person who related a succession of grievances."
Like Dr. Johnson, he addressed everybody, even
children, as " Sir."

I do not know that there are any other personal
traits to be recorded.

Hazlitt's mother, Grace Hazlitt, died in June 1837,
in her ninety-first year. *Her* mother, who lived till
1801, remembered the death of the late Protector,
Richard Cromwell, and was eleven years old when
George the First came over from Hanover to be our
King. Peggy the diarist died in Liverpool in 1844,

and the painter John, whose fortunes were not equal to his merits, died in May 1837. But one remark of his has come down to us, though his miniatures may still be seen — "No young man thinks he shall ever die."

CHAPTER XI

BOOKS of this kind usually end with a chapter entitled as above, but I have inscribed the word Character with trepidation. About Hazlitt's genius it were useless now to write; it speaks for itself in many a glowing page which proclaim him a great miscellaneous writer and a masterly and masterful critic. Of this critical aspect of Hazlitt, differences of opinion have existed, and will continue to exist. Landor, for example, writes: "Hazlitt's books are delightful to read, pleasant always, often elegant and affecting in the extreme. But I don't get much valuable criticism out of him." Heine, on the other hand, pronounces Hazlitt's mind to be not only brilliant, but deep, "a mixture of Diderot and Börne." On this matter the reader can and will judge for himself; he is hardly likely to be better qualified to form an opinion than Landor, or to express it than Heine.

But his character?

Ben Jonson says in his grave way that the main argument of character is a good life. This plenary argument cannot be used with much confidence on Hazlitt's behalf.

In his sketch of Horne Tooke, Hazlitt, who with a pen in his hand could be austere enough, observes: "Tooke's mind (so to speak) had no *religion* in it, and

226

very little of the 'moral qualities of genius.'" The same remark cannot be made of Hazlitt, who hated the materialism of the Whiggish and Erastian mind, and always thought nobly of man in the abstract, however heartily he hated Mr. Pitt, Lord Castlereagh, Lord Liverpool, and William Gifford, and a whole host of other people. Swift has told us that he hated Man, but loved John, Tom, and Dick; Hazlitt was disposed to reverse this process. But, unlike Tooke, he had (I think) religion in his mind, though it early disappeared from his life.

At some time or another Hazlitt got athwart the main current of existence, or as De Quincey, whose paper on Hazlitt is full of shrewdness, puts it, " he wilfully placed himself in collision with all the interests that were in the sunshine of this world, and with all the persons that were then powerful in England." Things early began to go wrong with him, and people, he knew not why, to eye him with the squint of suspicion. What had he done to be so hated? He had never a thought of personal aggrandisement; all his thoughts were of public affairs. A life freer from greed of gain, or taint of literary vanity,[1] is not to be found in the records of English literature. But he was always desperately in earnest; and found it not only hard, but plainly impossible, to put his political and philosophical convictions good-humouredly aside on occasions and be, for a season, all things to all men. He could not do it, and his inability to do it made him impatient of those who could and did. Lamb's

---

[1] See his letter to Mr. Napier, dated August 1818, declining an invitation to write on the *Drama* in the *Encyclopædia Britannica.* — *Selection from the Correspondence of Macvey Napier*, p. 21.

attitude of mind puzzled Hazlitt. He knew Lamb to
be, as indeed some of his less known writings show
him to have been, a sound and sane politician, with a
real grip of situations; and yet he was content not only
to live aloof from politics, but at peace with men who,
despite the noisy protestations of their early manhood,
had enrolled themselves in the great Army of Reaction.
This puzzled Hazlitt, and when he was puzzled he grew
angered, for his was a brooding, pondering nature. At
the bottom of his mind lay a deep, gloomy pool of
metaphysics, and into this pool he plunged from time
to time, always emerging more than ever in love with
abstract propositions and the hard core of thought.
He led a lonely life, thinking, thinking, thinking, and
the more he thought the darker grew the welkin.

Like the former tenant of 19 York Street, Hazlitt
became more and more a detached figure, out of keeping with his times — a republican without a populace —
for were not the populace on the other side? Often,
I doubt not, did Hazlitt mournfully repeat to himself
the lines dictated by Milton, old and blind, with
Charles Stuart at Whitehall —

" And what the people but a herd confused,
  A miscellaneous rabble who extol
  Things vulgar, and well weighed, scarce worth the praise?
  They praise, and they admire they know not what,
  And know not whom, but as one leads the other."

It cannot but be unfortunate when a man is doomed
to select for his hero the arch-enemy of his country.
It is wisest to hate your country's enemies. The
Church allows it, the National Anthem demands it,
and the experience of mankind approves it. Had

Hazlitt known all there was to be known about Bonaparte, he probably would have outlived a tragic devotion about which there was nothing undignified.   It
was no vulgar thing he extolled; for to Hazlitt, as to
Heine, Bonaparte represented the lordship of brain
and the divinity of brow as against hereditary
stupidity, insolence, and ugliness.   It was a terribly
costly delusion, but it was not otherwise than a
noble one.

Distracted by this anti-national passion, Hazlitt
became only too good a hater, and hate is a troublesome thing.

> " It rumples sleep;
> It settles on the dishes of the feast;
> It bites the fruit, it dips into the wine;
> I'd rather let my enemy hate me
> Than I hate him."

Hazlitt became as irritable as Rousseau; but as De
Quincey points out, in the paper before quoted, Hazlitt
viewed the personal affronts and casual slights he
fancied himself called upon to endure, not as being
aimed personally at him, but at his opinions.   " It was
not Hazlitt whom these wretches struck at; no, no;
it was democracy, or it was freedom, or it was Napoleon
whose shadow they saw behind Hazlitt, and Napoleon,
not for anything in him that might be really bad, but
in revenge of that consuming wrath against the thrones
of Christendom, for which (said Hazlitt) let us glorify
his name eternally."

In the letters of Wordsworth and Southey the
amazed reader encounters passions and prejudices at
least as furious on paper as those which devastated

Hazlitt. Southey's violence is boundless. In one of
his letters he declares it to be humiliating that Spain
should have produced two centuries ago half-a-dozen
men resolute in a mistaken cause to slay the Prince of
Orange at the sacrifice of their own lives, "and that
now she has not found one to aim a dagger at the heart
of Bonaparte." Wordsworth, too, had his disappointments. The Reform Bill preyed upon his health. The
pious Julius Hare, writing to Landor, after mentioning
this fact, proceeds to say : "Everybody said he seemed
to have grown ten years older in the last three months.
If the Bill does all the good which its most infatuated
advocates anticipate, it will hardly make amends for
this evil." Ten years off a poet's life would be perhaps a high price to pay even for a bloodless revolution,
but happily the country was not called upon to pay it.
Wordsworth had the good sense to get quite well again,
and lived far beyond the Psalmist's span. Southey, I
am sure, never really intended to advocate assassina-
tion, and was soon quite respectably employed in
compiling his *Book of the Church*. The fever in Hazlitt's
blood was not so easily allayed; and hence it is that
whilst the world has willingly forgotten Wordsworth's
prejudices, and has invested the poet's figure with
somewhat of the same dignity, calm, and repose as
cling to the famous statue of the seated Menander in
the Roman gallery, Hazlitt still figures in our minds
as a man struggling in the grasp of contending passions
and lifelong prejudices.

There are incidents in Hazlitt's life which are unpleasing in the extreme. We are told by Mr. R. L.
Stevenson's biographer that the *Liber Amoris* is believed
to have deprived the world of a Life of Hazlitt

from the feeling pen of "Tusitala." The loss is a heavy one.

It is perhaps no excuse to say, yet it is worth remembering, that Hazli t is his own accuser. Had he not turned traitor to himself, it is little or nothing we should have been able to urge against him save the holding until death of unpopular opinions. It does not follow as the night the day that lives were wholly free from shameful incidents because, as recorded by biographers, those who led them are made to appear as

> " Men that every virtue decks,
>   And women models of their sex,
>   Society's true ornament."

If it be replied that Hazlitt's lack of self-respect adds to his offences, a question is raised, I do not intend to pursue, how far and on what grounds sinful man is entitled to respect himself. In the eyes of the saints, at all events, the most repulsive of all figures is that of a well-groomed sinner, polite, reticent, self-controlled, self-contained, and brimful of " self-respect," a perfect piece of " polished ungodliness." Hazlitt at least was not that. His own hands tore down the veil which if left alone would have been the decent shroud of those failings, the frank revelation of which deprived him of an accomplished biographer.

As against this, it is only too true to say that Hazlitt's confessions, though entirely free from *fanfaronnade*, were not made in a penitential spirit, and display, even in their original published form, a mixture of coarseness and sentiment not a little disagreeable.

So far as the book *Liber Amoris* is concerned, it was a purely literary effort; an attempt to describe a man's

passion for a stony-hearted damsel. It was perhaps
worth the £100 John Hunt paid for it. It is the
facts that lie behind the book that are disagreeable,
how disagreeable we have unfortunately quite recently
been allowed to discover.

"The web of our life is of a mingled yarn, good and
ill together; our virtues would be proud if our faults
whipped them not; and our crimes would despair if
they were not cherished by our virtues." So said
Shakespeare, in a passage which, though it does not
pretend to be poetry, is sound criticism of life. It was
a very favourite quotation of Hazlitt's, who had no
more reason to be proud of his virtues than we have
the right to despair of his crimes.

How little is it we can know about the character of
a dead man we never saw! His books, if he wrote
books, will tell us something; his letters, if he wrote
any, and they are preserved, may perchance fling a
shadow on the sheet for a moment or two; a portrait
if painted in a lucky hour may lend the show of substance to our dim surmisings; the things he did must
carefully be taken into account; but, as a man is much
more than the mere sum of his actions, even these
cannot be relied upon with great confidence.

For the purpose of getting at any one's character, the
testimony of those who knew the living man in the
circumstances best calculated to reveal him as he truly
was, is of all the material likely to be within our reach
the most useful; *provided always* it is supplied by persons with sufficient insight into character to be able
to tell the truth, and *provided also* that they are both
permitted to tell it, and willing to do so. These pro-
visos, or some or one of them, destroy the value of

the greater part of the testimony of friends, whilst
that of enemies requires so much sifting as to be
practically useless.[1]

In Hazlitt's case we can fortunately call a witness
of the deepest insight into the finest shades of character, and of unimpeachable veracity; one who was
free to speak or to be silent as he chose, and who
knew all, or very nearly all, that we know about
Hazlitt, and a vast deal that we shall never know.
With Charles Lamb's characterisation of Hazlitt,
friendly but searching, I bring my task to its close: —

" From the other gentleman [Hazlitt] I neither expect nor
desire (as he is well assured) any such concessions. What
hath soured him, and made him suspect his friends of infi-
delity towards him, when there was no such matter, I know
not. I stood well with him for fifteen years (the proudest of
my life), and have ever spoken my full mind of him to some to
whom his panegyric must naturally be least tasteful. I never
in thought swerved from him; I never betrayed him; I never
slackened in my admiration of him; I was the same to him
(neither better nor worse), though he could not see it, as in the
days when he thought fit to trust me. At this instant he may
be preparing for me some compliment above my deserts, as he
has sprinkled many such among his admirable books, for
which I rest his debtor; or for anything I know or can guess
to the contrary, he may be about to read a lecture on my
weaknesses. He is welcome to them (as he was to my humble
hearth) if they can divert a spleen or ventilate a fit of sullen-
ness. I wish he would not quarrel with the world at the
rate he does; but the reconciliation must be affected by
himself, and I despair of living to see that day. But pro-

---

[1] " Characters should never be given by an historian unless he
knew the people whom he describes or copies from those who knew
them." — *Dr. Johnson*, see *Boswell* under year 1779. — A hard saying
for picturesque writers of history.

testing against much that he has written and some things
which he chooses to do; judging him by his conversations,
which I enjoyed so long and relished so deeply, or by his
books, in those places where no clouding passion intervenes,
I should belie my own conscience if I said less than that I
think W. H. to be in his natural and healthy state one of
the wisest and finest spirits breathing. So far from being
ashamed of that intimacy which was betwixt us, it is my
boast that I was able for so many years to have preserved
it entire ; and I think I shall go to my grave without finding,
or expecting to find, such another companion." [1]

[1] Letter of Elia to Southey. First printed in the *London Magazine* for October 1823.

INDEX

A

Abingdon, Mrs., 134.
Abstract Ideas, Essay, 73.
Actors and Acting (G. H. Lewes), 105.
Akenside, 129, 132.
Alexander and Campaspe (John Lyly), 133.
All-Foxden, 48, 51.
Alsager, Mr., 125.
America, The Peace with, 7–10.
American Rebels, 7.
Ancient Mariner (Coleridge), 53.
Angerstein Gallery, 178.
Antrim, 1, 2.
Arbuthnot, 137, 184.
Arcadia (Sidney's), 131.
Atlas, The, 208.

B

Bagehot, Walter, 57, 80, 129.
Ball, Sir Alexander, 61.
Bandon, Cork, 7.
Belsham, 31, 33.
Bentham, Jeremy, 97, 115, 124, 157, 196.
Berkeley, 45, 92, 99, 100, 101, 199.
"Betty Foy," 49.
Beyle, M., 191.
Bible, The, 137.
Biographia Literaria, 124.
Blackwood, Messrs. William and Sons, 168.
Blackwood's Magazine, 21, 158, 164, 165–168, 177, 201.
Blair, 131, 138, 168.
Blenheim, 92.
Boccaccio, 88, 89.

Bodleian Library, 92.
Börne, 226.
Boston, 11, 14, 15.
Boswell, 120.
Bourbons, The, 96, 186, 219.
Bridgewater, 48, 55.
Bristol, 50, 55.
Brougham, Mr., 160, 165, 171 note, 197.
Browne, Sir Thomas, 122, 131.
Bulwer, Edward Lytton, 73, 196.
Burke, Edmund, 33, 43, 54, 57, 80, 132, 144, 147, 151, 179.
Burleigh House, 35, 62, 68.
Burlington, U.S.A., 9.
Burney, Martin, 120, 223.
Burneys, The, 58.
Burns, Robert, 129, 172.
Butler, Bishop, 36, 45–46, 54, 92, 99, 199; Butler's *Sermons*, 46, 99, 199.
Byron, 139, 140, 196.

C

Caleb Williams, 54.
Camilla, 48.
Campbell, Thomas, 138, 144, 168, 196, 212.
Canning, Mr., 149, 160, 165.
Cape Cod, 14.
Carlisle, U.S.A., 10.
Carlyle, Thomas, 81, 115, 152, 185.
Caryl's *Commentaries on Job*, 22.
Castle Spectre (Monk Lewis), 50.
Castlereagh, Lord, 101, 127, 149, 161, 165, 227.
Causes of Methodism, Essay, 112.
Cavanagh, John, 159–162, 207.

235

Chalmers, Dr. Thomas, 172.
Chalmers's Poets, 210.
Chambers's *Encyclopædia of English Literature*, 133.
Champion, The, 110.
Chandler, Dr., 3.
Character of Pitt, 77–79, 95, 113, 151.
Characteristics (Hazlitt), 182–183.
—— (Shaftesbury), 70.
Characters of Shakespear's Plays, 110, 111, 113, 146.
Chatham, Earl of, 80, 151.
Chatterton, 128.
Chaucer, 129.
Chester, John, 52, 54, 55.
Child Angel (Charles Lamb), 92.
Christie, Mr. J. H., 166–168.
Church of England, 27, 202.
Clarke, C. Cowden, 213, 216.
Claude, 74, 130.
Clow, Professor, 3.
Cobbett, William, 90, 160, 197.
Colburn, Henry, 163.
Colburn's *Magazine*, 196.
Coleraine, 1.
Coleridge, Hartley, 66.
—— Samuel Taylor, 37, 38–55, 56–58, 61, 66, 77, 83, 95, 96, 98, 99, 113, 122, 123, 126, 131, 141, 142, 150, 160, 169 note, 196, 198–201.
Collins, 128, 129, 132, 211.
"Complaint of a Poor Indian Woman," 49.
Comus, Milton, 36.
Conciones ad Populum (Coleridge), 141.
Confederacy, The, 134.
Confessions (Rousseau), 35.
Congreve, 61, 133–134, 184.
Conversations of James Northcote, 180, 212–213.
Copley, 13.
Corehouse, Lord (Mr. Cranston), 172 note.

Coriolanus, 105, 110, 113.
Corporation Acts, 21, 29.
Coulson, Mr., 157.
Country Wife, 134.
Covent Garden Theatre, 108.
Cowper, 53, 73, 127, 129, 130.
Crediton, 152.
Criticisms on Art, 61–64, 67–69, 70–72.
Croker, Mr., 149, 161.
Cumberland, 66, 71.
"Cupid and my Campaspe played," 133.

D

Dante, 137, 191.
Darling, Dr., 220.
Darwin, Dr., 129.
De Foe, 4, 217; Wilson's Life of, 217.
De Quincey, 83, 196, 207, 227, 229.
Diderot, 226.
Dignum (The Singer), 26.
"Don Quixote," 36, 117, 176.
Donne, 122, 132.
Dorchester, U.S.A., 14–15.
Drummond of Hawthornden, 133.
Drury Lane Theatre, 55, 108, 109.
Dryden, 132, 143 note, 210–211.
Dyer, George, 118.

E

Edinburgh, 171, 172, 173.
Edinburgh Review, 124, 144, 145, 157, 160, 169 note, 171 note, 193, 208, 217.
Edwards, Jonathan, 99, 100, 181.
Egotism, Essay, 208 note.
Elegy (Gray's), 132.
Elgin marbles, 64.
Elliston, Mr., 55.
Eloquence of the British Senate, 80, 95, 151.
Encyclopædia Britannica, 80.
English Students at Rome, Essay, 72.

Entrance of Christ into Jerusalem (Haydon), 50.
Essays of Elia, 118, 165.
Essays on the Fine Arts (Richardson), 62, 178, 179.
Examiner, The, 55 note, 104, 110, 111, 113, 120, 169 note, 208, 216.
Excursion (Wordsworth), 120.

F

Farquhar, 34, 133, 134.
Fashion, Essay on, 117 note.
Fawcett, Joseph, 35–37, 77.
Fielding, 36, 54, 61, 121.
Fight, The, 112–113, 119, 162–163, 178.
FitzGerald, Edward, 211 note.
Flaxman, 179, 217.
Florence, 193–195.
Fonblanque, Mr., 216–217.
Foresight (Congreve), 133–134.
Forster, John, 107, 195.
Fortnightly Review, 176–177.
Fox, Charles, 54, 65, 80, 151.
France, 184, 185–188.
Franklin, Benjamin, 6.
Free Thoughts on Public Affairs, 76, 77, 113.
French Revolution, 6, 32, 59, 88, 96, 136, 139, 217–218.
Friend, The, 61, 141.
Friends and Acquaintances (Patmore), 126, 223–224.
Froude, J. A., 192.

G

Garrick, 134.
Gateacre, 69.
Gay, 127, 132.
Gebir (Landor), 194.
Gifford, William, 74, 77, 113, 114, 116, 143, 146–149, 151, 164, 168, 196, 197, 227.
Gil Blas, 36, 67, 117, 122.
Gilfillan, George, 197.
Glasgow, 171; University of, 3, 41.
Godwin, 43, 44, 58, 59, 92, 157.

Godwins, The, 4, 35, 39, 58.
Goethe, 137.
Goldsmith, 129.
Gosse, Edmund, 179, 180, 213.
Gray, 54, 128, 129, 132, 211.

H

Hackney Theological College, 31, 32, 77, 101.
Hagley, Miss, 26.
Hamlet, 109, 110.
Hare, Julius, 195, 230.
Harmer Hill, 46.
Hartleap Well, 140.
Hartley, 31, 199.
Harvard, U.S.A., 11.
Haydon, 40 note, 50, 116, 159 note, 176, 179.
Hayley, 129.
Hazlitt, William, his name, 1; his ancestry, 1, 2; his father, 3; birth at Maidstone, 6; accompanies the family to America, 7; his life in America, 7–16; return to England, 7–15; lives with the family in London, 17–19; removes to Wem in Shropshire, 19; his education, 19, 20, 21; interest in theology and politics, 21, 22, 23, 24; visit to Liverpool, 24–28; studies French, 25; first visit to the theatre, 26; he enters Hackney Theological College, 30; his studies there, 30, 31, 32; goes back to Wem, 32; his reading, 33–35; meets Coleridge, 40; visit to Nether Stowey, 48–55; resolves to become a painter, 62; goes to Paris to study art, 62, 63; becomes itinerant portrait painter, 66; abandons painting as a profession, 71; his first book, *Essay in Defence of the Natural Disinterestedness of the Human Mind*, 73; *Free*

Thoughts on Public Affairs, 76; abridgment of Tucker's Light of Nature, 79; The Eloquence of the British Senate, 80; Reply to the Essay on Population by the Rev. T. R. Malthus, 81; his marriage, 86, 115–117; goes to Winterslow, 90; writes "A New and Improved" English Grammar, 90; Memoirs of Holcroft, 92; birth of a son, 92; returns to London, 94; his friends and acquaintances, 95, 117–121; lectures on Modern Philosophy, 98; becomes a reporter in the Gallery of the House of Commons, 101; alcoholic excess and total abstinence, 101, 222; becomes a dramatic critic, 104; Characters of Shakespear's Plays, 110; View of the English Stage, 125; Round Table, 111, 112; lectures at the Surrey Institution, 125–142; Letter to William Gifford, 146–149; Table-Talk, 163; contributes to the London Magazine, 165; divorce, 169–174; lectures in Glasgow, 171; the Miss Walker episode, 173–178; Liber Amoris, 176, 177, 178; Characteristics, 181–183; second marriage,183; visit to the Continent, 184; Notes of a Journey through France and Italy, 184; return to England, 195; Spirit of the Age, 196; Life of Napoleon, 207; The Plain Speaker, 208; Hazlitt's Select Poets, 210; Conversations of James Northcote, 212; his death, 220; personal traits, 221–224; his fondness of rackets and fives, 159–162; his income, 124, 125, 208, 216, 220; his character and genius, 226–234; his aversions, 227–230; his frankness, 231; his political opinions, 29–32, 95, 140, 193–194, 227, 228; philosophical speculation, 30, 32, 56, 61, 73–76, 92, 98–101, 227, 228; his qualifications as a dramatic critic, 105–111; as an essayist, 111, 112; as a critic of poetry, 130–142; as an art critic 178, 179, 180; permanence of his influence, 145, 146.

Hazlitt, William (Hazlitt's father), 2–16, 17, 19–24, 25–27, 31, 33, 41, 42, 43, 56, 65, 69, 70, 71, 73, 83, 95, 151–154.

—— Mrs. Grace (his mother), 5, 7, 15, 35, 151–154, 173, 174, 219, 220, 224.

—— John (his grandfather), 1, 2.

—— Mrs. Margaret (his grandmother), 1–3, 41.

—— Colonel John (his uncle), 2, 10.

—— James (his uncle), 2, 3.

—— John (his brother), 6, 7, 10, 12–15, 18–21, 32, 35, 57, 71, 83, 87, 95, 225.

—— Loftus (his brother), 6.

—— Margaret (his sister), 6–9, 10, 11, 12, 13, 15, 18–21, 151–154, 173, 224.

—— Harriet (his sister), 7.

—— Esther (his sister), 8.

—— Mrs. (née Sarah Stoddart, his first wife), 58, 61, 86–90, 91–93, 115–117, 124, 151, 169, 170–174, 183, 186, 219.

—— Mrs. (née Mrs. Bridgewater, his second wife), 183, 184, 186, 195.

—— William (his son), 1, 92–93, 116, 117, 150, 151, 169, 173, 178, 186, 195, 212, 219, 220.

——, John (his younger son), 117.

—— W. Carew (his grandson), 1, 3, 56, 69 note, 84, 117, 178, 195, 221, 224.

Hazlitt's Select Poets, 210–211.

Head of the Old Woman (painting), 67–69.

Heine, 226, 229.

Herrick, 133.

Hessey, Mr., 220.

Hingham, U.S.A., 12–15.

Hinton, Mr., 153.

History of the Court of Chancery (Joseph Parkes), 119.

Hobbes, 29, 75, 92, 99.

Holcroft, Thomas, 35, 58, 92, 123.

—— Mrs., 92.

Holcrofts, The, 58.

Holy Alliance, 88, 96.

Homer, 136, 137.

Hood, 196.

Hook, 196.

Hoppner, Mr., 149.

Horne, Mr. R. H., 220, 221.

Hours in a Library (Leslie Stephen), 74, 207.

House of Commons, 101–104.

Hume, David, 45, 179.

Hume, Joseph, 84.

Humphry Clinker, 36.

Hunt, John, 150, 158, 177, 232.

—— Henry Leigh, 157.

—— Leigh, 95, 111, 112, 124, 125, 148, 151, 156–158, 166, 210.

Hunt and Cowden Clarke, 184, 213, 218.

I

Imaginary Conversations (Landor), 193, 195.

Indian Jugglers, Essay, 159–163.

Ireland, Mr. Alexander, 73.

Italy, 188–195.

J

"Jacob's Ladder" (painting), 91.

Jeffrey, 124, 157, 177, 220.

John Buncle, 112, 121, 178.

Johnson, Dr. Samuel, 33 note, 45, 54, 58, 100, 101, 121, 125, 127–130, 222, 224, 233 note.

Johnson, Mr. (publisher), 73, 80.

Jonson, Ben, 133, 226.

Jordan, Mrs., 74, 134.

Julia de Roubigné (Mackenzie), 71.

Junius, 54, 122, 160.

K

Kean, Edmund, 107–110, 223.

Keats, 128, 131.

Kemble, 26, 105, 109, 110, 149.

Keswick, 67.

Kippis, Dr., 6.

Knowledge of Character, Essays, 175.

Knowles, Sheridan, 174, 176, 177.

L

La Rochefoucauld, 182.

Lalla Rookh, 139.

Lamb, Mary, 86, 87, 88, 90, 91, 93, 117, 120.

Lamb, Charles, 27, 57, 58, 71, 83–86, 88, 90–92, 93, 94, 107, 117, 120–123, 124, 131, 133, 157, 158, 159, 165, 198, 207, 210, 216, 217, 219, 220, 228, 233, 234.

Lamb and Hazlitt (W. Carew Hazlitt), 84, 91.

L'Amour (M. Beyle), 191.

Lana, 65.

Landor, 33, 96, 97, 107, 133, 140, 193–195, 226, 230; Forster's *Life of Landor*, 195.

Lay of the Laureate (Southey), 104.

Lectures on the English Poets, 126, 143, 146.

—— *on the English Comic Writers*, 126.

—— *on the Dramatic Literature of the Age of Elizabeth*, 126, 133.

—— *on the Rise and Progress of Modern Philosophy*, 98.

—— *on the Law of Nature and Nations* (Mackintosh), 59–60.

Letter to a Noble Lord (Burke), 33, 34.

Letter to William Gifford, Esq., 114, 146–150.

Lewes, G. H. 105, 109.

Lewis, Mr. David, 17.

—— Monk, 50.

Liber Amoris, 169, 171, 173–178, 230, 231.

Liberal, The, 55 note, 172.

Liberty and Necessity, Lecture, 99, 100.

Light of Nature pursued (Tucker), 79, 181.

Liston, 106.

Literary Remains (Hazlitt's), 30, 55 note, 98, 126–128, 221.

—— Studies (Bagehot), 129.

Liverpool, 24–27.

—— Lord, 227.

Llangollen Vale, 47.

Locke, 92, 99, 184, 194.

Lockhart, 166–168; Lang's Life of Lockhart, 167 note, 168.

Loftus, Mrs. (Hazlitt's grandmother), 5, 18, 224.

London, 15, 17–19, 31, 32, 57, 58, 86, 94, 95, 98, 115–117, 187, 188, 189, 196, 208, 217, 219.

—— Magazine, 120, 164, 165, 178, 208, 233, 234.

—— Weekly Review, 208.

Longmans, Messrs., 83.

Lorraine, Claude, 91.

Louvre, The, 56–72, 185, 186, 189, 192.

Love for Love, 134.

—— in Many Masks, 26.

Lowe, Sir Hudson, 116.

Lyly, John, 133.

Lyrical Ballads, 48, 53, 57.

M

Macaulay, 4, 19, 124, 191.

Macbeth, 109, 110.

Mackenzie, 71.

Mackintosh, Sir James, 43, 58–60, 73, 74, 80, 165.

Mad Mother, 49.

Madonna Pia, story of, 191, 192.

Maidstone, 6.

Malta, 60.

Malthus, Rev. T. R., 81–83, 90, 184, 196.

Man of Feeling (Mackenzie), 71.

Manchester, 67.

Manning, 87.

Marriage laws of England and Scotland, 170, 171.

Marshfield, Gloucestershire, 5.

Martineau, Dr., 24.

Marvell, 132, 210.

Medwin, Captain, 206.

Memoirs of William Hazlitt, 6, 117, 154, 156–158, 159 note.

Merry England, Essay, 206.

Midsummer Night's Dream, 110.

"Millamant," 134.

Miller, Mr. John, 73.

Milton, 36, 54, 74, 90, 97, 98, 115, 122, 126, 128, 130, 132, 171, 228; Milton's Sonnets, 97.

Mr. H—— (Lamb), 84, 86.

Monody to Chatterton (Coleridge), 38, 198.

Montagu, Basil, 158, 220.

Montaigne, 112.

Moor, Dr., 3.

Moore, Tom, 138.

Moral and Political Philosophy (Paley), 47.

More, Hannah, 127, 129.

Morning Chronicle, 103, 104, 109, 110, 126, 184, 208.

Morning Post, 77.

Mounsey, George, 118, 119.

Munden, 134.

Murray, Lindley, 90.

Murray, John, 149, 164.

N

Napier: *Selection from the Correspondence of Macvey Napier*, 227 note.

Napoleon Bonaparte, 65, 96, 106, 111, 116, 125, 131, 139, 182, 185, 186, 194, 229, 230; Hazlitt's *Life of Napoleon*, 159, 196, 206, 207, 211, 213-219.

Natural Disinterestedness of the Human Mind, 46, 56, 58, 73, 74-76.

Nether Stowey, 48-55.

New and Improved Grammar of the English Tongue, 90.

New Eloïse (Rousseau), 35.

New Monthly Magazine, 162, 208, 211.

New School of Reform, Essay, 26 note, 208 note.

New Times, 166.

New York, 8-9.

Newman, John Henry, 81, 136.

No Song, no Supper (play), 26.

Northcote, James, 62, 116, 121, 179, 212, 213.

Notes of a Journey through France and Italy, 181, 184-193.

O

Ode to the Departing Year (Coleridge), 38.

On a Landscape by Poussin, 163.

On Actors and Acting, 107, 108.

On Consistency of Opinion, 31, 32.

On Court Influence, 22, 23, 24.

On going a Journey, 163.

On Patronage and Puffing, 96, 163.

On reading Old Books, 71.

On the Conduct of Life, 212.

On the Conversation of Authors, 121-124, 208 note.

On the Difference between Writing and Speaking, 102, 103, 208, 209.

On the Fear of Death, 154, 163, 177.

On the Feeling of Immortality in Youth, 28, 29.

On the Ignorance of the Learned, 162.

On the Pleasures of Painting, 61, 62, 63, 64, 67, 71.

On the Political State of Man, 30, 31.

On the Principles of Human Action. See *Natural Disinterestedness of the Human Mind*.

On the Tendency of Sects, 24, 112.

Orleans Gallery, 61, 62.

Ossian, 137, 139.

Othello, 109, 110.

Oxford, 91, 188.

—— *in the Vacation* (Lamb), 92.

P

Paine, Thomas, 45.

Paley, 46, 118.

Palmer, Jack, 106.

Paradise Lost, 36, 97, 122.

Paradise Regained, 122.

Paradox and Commonplace, Essay, 154, 155, 156.

Paris, 61-65, 185-188, 194.

Parkes, Joseph, 119.

Pastoral Ballad (Shenstone), 36.

Patmore, P. G., 125, 126, 164, 167, 168, 174, 177, 178, 220, 223, 224.

Paul and Virginia, 48.

People with one Idea, Essay, 130.

Peregrine Pickle, 34, 185.

Perry, Mr., 103, 104, 125.

—— Sir Erskine, 103.

Perry, Miss, 103.

Persons one would wish to have seen, Essay, 120.

Peter Bell (Wordsworth), 51.

"Peter Martyr" (Titian), 179.

Peterborough, 5.

Philadelphia, 9, 10.

Piggott, Robert, 119.

Pitt, William, 5, 54, 58, 77-79, 151, 182, 227.

Pleasures of Memory (Rogers), 138.

R

Plain Speaker, The, 26 note, 102, 103, 121-124, 165, 208, 209.
Plunkett, 103, 165.
Poems on the Naming of Places (Wordsworth), 48.
Political Essays, 22, 23, 24, 80, 104, 130, 140, 150, 196.
Ponsonby, 165.
Pope, 54, 128, 132, 137.
Porson, 118, 119.
Posthumous Fame, Essay, 112.
Poussin, 64, 66.
Presbyterianism, English, 4.
Price, Dr., 3, 7, 31.
Priestley, Dr., 6, 11, 25, 29, 33, 100, 199.
Prior, Dr., 3.
—— Matthew, 132.
Procter, 175, 176, 210, 220, 223; *Charles Lamb*, 101 note; *Autobiographical Fragments*, 176.
Provoked Husband, 62.
Provoked Wife, 134.

Q

Quarterly Review, 77, 104, 113, 120, 143, 147, 151, 160, 164, 169.

R

Railton, Miss, 71.
Raphael, 62, 66, 70, 189.
Recruiting Officer (Farquhar) 34.
Rees, Dr., 31.
Relapse, The, 134.
Religious Musings (Coleridge), 200.
Rembrandt, 21, 35, 62, 66, 68, 70, 178.
Remorse (Coleridge), 55.
Reply to the Essay on Population, 81, 83, 95.
Repository, The, 153, 154.
Reynell, Mr., 219.
—— Miss, 219.
Reynolds, Mr., 157.
—— Sir Joshua, 18, 58, 68, 179.
Richard the Third, 109, 110.

Richardson, 34, 35, 54.
Rickmanns, The, 58.
Rise and Progress of Modern Philosophy Lectures, 98-101.
Road to Ruin (Holcroft), 92.
Robinson, Crabb, 57, 92.
Rogers, Samuel, 138.
Rome, 188-192.
Romeo, 110.
Romilly, Sir Samuel, 165.
Round Table, 24, 77-79, 104, 112, 113, 120, 129, 146, 148, 149.
Rousseau, 8, 25, 35, 184, 213, 229.
Rowe, Mr. (Unitarian minister), 38.
Rubens, 64, 178.
Ruskin, 202.

S

St. Andrew's Church, Holborn, 86.
St. Anne's, Soho, 220, 221.
St. James's Chronicle, 33.
St. Peter's, Rome, 190, 191.
Salisbury, 58, 90.
Salisbury Plain, 90, 130.
School for Scandal, 106.
Scott, John, 166-168.
—— Sir Walter, 52, 74, 140, 143, 196, 201-205, 207, 214, 215, 217.
Scott, Racine, and Shakespeare, Essay, 204, 205.
Seasons (Thomson's), 53.
Select Discourses (William Hazlitt the elder), 28, 73.
Shaftesbury, 70.
Shakespeare, 54, 65, 98, 106, 107, 110, 111, 126, 128, 133, 136, 171, 232; *Sonnets*, 65.
Shelburne, Lord, 7.
Shelley, 154, 155, 156, 158.
Shenstone, 36.
Shepherd, Dr., 69; Sally Shepherd, 69.
Sheridan, 135.
Short Studies (Froude), 192.
Shrewsbury, 33, 34, 38, 39, 44-46.

Shronell, 2.
"Shylock," 109.
Siddons, Mrs., 8, 74, 106, 130, 213.
Sidney, Sir Philip, 46, 122, 131.
Sienna, 192.
"Sir John Brute," 134.
Skeffington, Sir George, 70.
Sketches and Essays, 105 note, 117 note
Smith, Adam, 3.
—— Mr. Horatio, 167.
—— Mr. D. Nicol, 168.
Smollett, 121, 122.
Soho, 219, 220.
Some Remarks on the Systems of Hartley and Helvetius, 58, 73.
South, 45.
Southampton Buildings, Holborn, 174, 175.
Southampton Coffee House, 118.
Southey, 50, 66, 74, 96, 104, 120, 129, 131, 143, 149, 150, 151, 159, 194, 195, 196, 229, 230.
Spenser, 129, 191.
Spirit of Obligations, Essay, 208 note.
Spirit of the Age, 59, 60, 114, 115, 129, 147, 148, 196, 204.
Stamford, 171, 174.
Stephen, Mr. Leslie, 74, 207.
Sterne, 36, 117.
Stevenson, R. L., 208 note, 230.
Stoddart, Dr. John, 58, 60, 61, 87, 90, 166, 167, 187.
Stonehenge, 90, 183.
Stuarts, The, 191, 202.
Suckling, 133.
Suett, the actor, 26.
Surrey Institution, 125.
Swift, 128, 131, 132, 227.
Sybilline Leaves, 49.

T

Table-Talk, 154–156, 159–162, 163, 164, 175, 177, 208.
Talfourd, Mr. Justice, 96, 107, 126–128, 134, 217, 221–223.

Taylor and Hessey, 186.
Taylor, Jeremy, 54, 74, 131.
Télémaque, 25.
Tennyson, 163.
Test Act, 21, 25, 29.
Thackeray, 103.
The Free Admission, Essay, **219**.
"The Fudge Family," 138.
The Sick Chamber, Essay, 219.
The Sublime and Beautiful (Burke), 179.
Thomson, James, 53, 172.
Thorn, 49.
Tierney, 165.
Times, The, 125.
Tintoret, 66.
Tipperary, 1, 2.
Titian, 8, 13, 62, 63, 64, 65, 91, 130, 179, 213.
Tom Jones, 34, 47.
Tooke, Horne, 90, 197, 226, 227.
Toulmin, Dr., 55.
Tracys, The, of Liverpool, 24, 25, 27, 28, 73.
Traill, Mr., 167.
Tucker, Abraham, 79, 80, 95, 181.
Tuileries, 188.

U

Unitarianism, 3, 4, 10, 11, 24, 30, 31, 33.
United States of America, 7–16.

V

Vanbrugh, 133–135, 184.
Vandyke, 74, 178.
Vevey, 206.
View of the English Stage, 104, 107–111, 125.
Viny, Mr., of Tenterden, 6.
Virgil, 53.

W

Walker, Miss, 169, 170, 174–177.
Walter, Mr., of the *Times*, 125.
Walthamstow, 35.
Walworth, 17–18.
Warton's *Sonnets*, 65, 131.

Washington, General, 10.
Watchman, The, 38, 141.
Waterloo, 96.
Waverley Novels, 74, 140, 184, 202–205.
Way of the World (Congreve), 134.
Wedgwood, Thomas, 43, 44.
Wells, Mr., 220.
Wem, 8, 17–37, 39, 46, 56, 57, 83, 95, 151, 152.
Werther, 139.
Wesley, John, 90.
Weymouth, U.S.A., 11–14.
Whitbread, 165.
White, Mr., 220.
Why Distant Objects Please, Essay, 17, 18.
Wiche, Mr., 6.
Wilberforce, 165.
Williams, Mrs., the actress, 26.
Wilson, Professor, 21, 164.
—— Effingham, 217.

—— Walter, 217.
Winterslow, 19, 58, 87, 90–93, 152, 183, 196, 208, 211; *Winterslow, Essays*, 28, 29, 31, 32, 55 note, 152.
Wisbeach, 5, 35.
Wither, 133.
Wollstonecrafts, The, 58; Mrs. Wollstonecraft, 35.
Wordsworth, Dorothy, 66.
—— William, 37, 43, 48–51, 53, 56, 57, 61, 66, 96, 97, 120, 132, 140, 154, 160, 172, 179, 194, 196, 210, 229, 230.
Wycherley, 133–135.

Y

Yates, Mr., 25, 28.
Yellow Dwarf (Leigh Hunt), 124, 151.
York Street, Westminster, 97, 115, 116, 126, 170.
Young, 128, 129, 132, 211.